Deprogrammed

by S.S. Riley

For Norma

I'm just the messenger,
please don't shoot!

With lots of love,
Shelley

RoseDog🐾Books
PITTSBURGH, PENNSYLVANIA 15238

RoseDog Books
585 Alpha Drive
Suite 103
Pittsburgh, PA 15238
Visit our website at www.rosedogbookstore.com

ISBN: 978-1-4809-7046-5
eISBN: 978-1-4809-7069-4

Dedicated to:

First and foremost, to the Father, Son and Holy Ghost,
Without whom we can do nothing.

Secondly, to every person alive on the face of the planet.
I love you and pray that as you read this,
every faculty you possess will be opened to the Truth.
Not as it applies to you and your life,
but as itapplies to the Divine Will of God, our Creator.

Chapter 1

"but be ye transformed by the renewing of your mind,"
In Romans 12:2

It knocked her for a loop is what it did. It literally sent her to her knees mentally for close to a year. When Kizzy earnestly prayed for her eyes to be opened and for her ears to hear and for her mind to understand and for the Lord to give her whatever little knowledge and wisdom He wanted her to have, she had no idea what she was in for.

It never hit her like a sledgehammer. It was more like a progressive input of information. A little here and a bit more there, gradually adding up to the fact that we are little more than a heathen, paganistic, idol worshipping nation.

"Thou art near in their mouth, and far from their reins."
In Jeremiah 12:2

It hit Kizzy hard. It was true. She had been doing whatever she wanted for a very long time, chalking it up to the way of the world. Often she heard it said, "It's the 20th century, it's the 21st century, things have changed. God understands." (Yes, it was that long.)

She never fully agreed. She knew that God never changed. His decrees and demands were never updated with the times. Part of her problem was the culture, the times she had grown up in. That's just the way it was, how it had always been. How it would always be…or so she thought.

It was all acceptable. Everyone seemed to be on the same path.

Yes, God did understand. He understood that we were imperfect sinners, and we seemed to like it that way. He also understood that we were completely disobedient to His Commands and to the Word of His Son. He also knew something else.

"He hath blinded their eyes, and hardened their heart;"
In John 12:40

"and the rest were blinded."
In Romans 11:7

"because that darkness hath blinded his eyes."
In 1 John 2:11

Kizzy knew that God punished people for their disobedience. Maybe that is part of the reason there is so much misery in the world. She had more than her share of hard times in her life. Often Kizzy knew that a particular problem was the direct result of her disobedient actions.

If people continue to walk in sin and rebellion despite the punishment of the Lord, will He allow them to be blinded as the disbelieving Jews were? There was a reason for their blindness; what is the reason for hers? She believed herself to be a Christian, she loved God and the Lord Jesus Christ. But she just wouldn't listen.

"To deliver such an one unto Satan for the destruction of the
flesh, that the spirit may be saved in the day of the Lord Jesus."
1 Corinthians 5:5

Had she been delivered to Satan? By reading around this Scripture, Kizzy knew it pertained to sexual disobedience. But…couldn't it be applied to any unruly behavior? Drunkenness, gluttony, lying, laziness, cheating, envy, idol worship, drug use? Kizzy was sure it could be and at different times in her life was guilty of a few of them.

When she was younger, she had been in a car wreck that had nearly taken her life. It was only recently that a vague thought had been playing in her mind. Had Satan been trying to kill her at the time? Were two other people killed because of her? Why? Was it because when she was a small child, playing alone in the woods, she had heard a male voice in her head tell her that someday she would do something important? Was that something important related to her almost nervous breakdown the past summer when she believed she was going crazy?

Kizzy had wondered at the time if a crazy person knew they were crazy, or if they just were and didn't care. Through it all, Kizzy cried out to the Lord for help.

When the Light finally started to shine in the darkness, it was as if a spotlight had been put on the Word of God. Things she had read over and over again finally started to take on meaning. It was like she was reading it for the first time.

> *"Not every one that saith unto Me, Lord,*
> *Lord, shall enter into the Kingdom of Heaven;"*
> *In Matthew 7:21*

This scared Kizzy. All who believe and are baptized will be saved, but are there different parts to Heaven? She believed that what Jesus said was true. unlike a certain Church she had attended for a while, "We take the Bible gravely, but not exactly." She could never figure out what the difference was. She decided she better just take it exactly to be on the safe side. Personal choice on her part.

If you were saved, but not allowed into the Kingdom of Heaven, where did you go? The meek shall inherit the earth, but people like Kizzy had never been meek. And with what it seemed the Lord was asking her to do, it looked like she never would be. That seemed to be out of the question. So what then? Lord, what should Kizzy do?

> *"but he that doeth the Will of My Father which is in Heaven."*
> *In Matthew 7:21*

"And why call Me, Lord, Lord,
and do not the things which I say?"
Luke 6:46

"Behold, to obey is better than sacrifice,
and to hearken than the fat of rams."
In 1 Samuel 15:22

Kizzy prayed and asked, "What is Your Will, Father?" She truly wanted to start pleasing Him. Obedience. That's it. Obey. So…where do we start? The Ten Commandments maybe?

1. *Thou shalt have no other gods before me.*

2. *Thou shall not make unto thee any graven image, or any likeness of any thing that is in the Heaven above, or that is in the earth beneath, or that is in the water under the earth: Thou shalt not bow down thyself to them, nor serve them: for I the Lord thy God am a jealous God visiting the iniquity of the fathers upon the children unto the third and fourth generation of them that hate Me; and shewing mercy unto thousands of them that love Me, and keep My Commandments.*

3. *Thou shalt not take the Name of the Lord Thy God in vain, for theLord will not hold him guiltless that taketh His Name in vain.*

4. *Remember the Sabbath Day, to keep It Holy. Six days thou shalt labour, and do all thy work: but the seventh day is the Sabbath of the Lord thy God: in it thou shalt not do any work, thou, nor thy son, nor thy daughter, thy manservant, nor thy maidservant, nor thy cattle,nor thy stranger that is within thy gates: For in six days the Lord made Heaven and earth, the sea, and all that in them is, and rested the seventh day: wherefore the Lord blessed the Sabbath Day, and hallowed it.*

5. *Honour thy father and thy mother: that thy days may be long upon the land which the Lord thy God giveth thee.*

6. *Thou shalt not kill.*

7. *Thou shalt not commit adultery.*

S.S. Riley

8. *Thou shalt not steal.*

9. *Thou shalt not bear false witness against thy neighbour.*

10. *Thou shalt not covet thy neighbour's house, thou shalt not covet thy neighbour's wife nor his manservant, nor his maidservant, nor his ox, nor his ass, nor any thing that is thy neighbour's.*

Exodus 20:2-17

Kizzy read them, then read them again. Funny, well, not really so funny as sad; she claimed to be of the faith for most of her life, but if asked, she wouldn't have been able to remember all ten. And be obedient to them? How could you be if you didn't even know what they were?

Yes, there was the conscience involved, but so what? Kizzy had heard someone once say the conscience was like a rough stone being rolled down a stream. Eventually, with enough rolling around in the brain, the rough stone became a smooth pebble and didn't bother you anymore. You became immune to guilt after so many times of the same sin.

So many times of rolling it around and knocking the painful corners off . So many times of making lame excuses and blaming other people.

Armed with this new, very precious gift of illumination, Kizzy thought about each of the Commandments and how she needed to implement them in her life.

1. "No other gods BEFORE Me." Kiz wondered if that meant it was okay to have other gods if they didn't take precedence over the One True God. Probably not. Then she pondered what other gods might be. As the list developed in her mind, it became massive, with seemingly no end and she began to get a headache. People were putting anything and everything before God. In most cases she was familiar with, things left little or no time for the Lord. She realized with shame that she was as guilty as the next person. Kiz didn't know the exact moment it had happened, but somehow she knew that none of this was a game. It was all or nothing. She was done with what seemed in her mind to be a game of dodge-ball

with God. The time had come to get serious. She expected a lot of setbacks along the way, but Kizzy was determined to put the Lord first in her life in all things. And there were many things.

2. "Make no graven image." She was guilty of that. Arts and crafts that were of no practical use. How would you serve a graven image? By giving it a prominent place in the home where it would be given the most attention? Where it would look it's best? Had she bowed down to them by being proud of what she had done? She began to get a sick feeling in her stomach. It was time to clean house. All the while she was glad she hadn't hated God. Or had she? By being disobedient to His Word, what had she shown Him all these years? That what He said made no difference to her? Kizzy fell on her knees in remorse. And there was that pesky "but if" again. Would mercy really only be shown to them that love Him and keep His Commandments? There it was in black and white. Kizzy thought back through what she knew of the Bible; there seemed to be quite a few "but if you don'ts" in there. It was also obvious to her that people cannot keep those Commandments entirely. That is why Jesus came - to show Grace and allow us to be forgiven. God knows who tries and who doesn't. If a Christian deliberately and with much thought breaks Commandments, are they forgiven? Does it show the Lord our God that we are going our own way, not His? They are Commandments by the way, not merely suggestions. Kiz was quiet and thoughtful for a very long period of time.

3. "Do not Take the Lord's Name in vain." At first, this one looked easy to Kiz. She had always been told and always believed that it meant using the Lord's Name as a cussword. It had always repulsed her when she heard the Lord's Name used that way, so she didn't think she had done it. She did though, sometime say the words "Oh, my God." It was never meant in a mean, dirty or degrading way, more as a plea for assistance. But, just as she thought she was safe here, the oddest sensation came over her. It seemed as though her mind went blank. Kizzy stared at the words. Take. Take. Take the Lord's Name in vain. Take. Take the Name of the Lord in vain. As the realization of what it was saying became clear, a cold wave of shudders went through her. The Church was the bride of Christ. When we became a member of the Church, or faith family, we were joined in as that bride. "Lord, please forgive us." Just as when, in the old days, a couple

(man and woman) were wed, she took his last name signifying they were one flesh. She took. She had taken his name. Do we become the bride of Christ, take His Good Name and then soil it? Do we take His Name and then continue our quest for fornication, adultery, money, success, lying, appearance and all the rest of what the world has to offer? Uh oh. Should she, in the broadest sense of the words, call herself Mrs. Kizzy Christ? Had she, in all these years taken the name of the Lord in vain? What did vain mean? According to Webster's it meant having no real value, worthless, without effect, futile. No wonder Jesus said that not all who call Him Lord will enter the Kingdom of Heaven. We, being married to our Lord and Savior, were pretty much tramps. Kiz needed some real big attitude adjustments on an issue she perceived as simple. It wasn't. Onto her knees she went.

4. "Remember the Sabbath to keep It holy." Of course she hadn't done that either. Satan was very powerful and cunning. It felt to her like she piddled around lazily all week and then on Sunday all these things popped into her head that needed to be done. Was it evil influence or a subconscious thing? Whatever it was, Sunday was always a catch-up day. It shouldn't be. She was determined to change that. Yes, there were a few things that needed to be done on Sunday. The dogs had to be taken out, fed and given water. Kiz realized a lot needed to change in her life. It couldn't be done overnight. The "not making strangers work" thing bothered her. There would be no more money spent on Sunday. Not even for gas in her car. The Lord intended It to be a day of rest for all. She wasn't helping by making It her shopping day. She would just add things to her list and do them on Monday. God had hallowed the day. Kizzy looked the word up in her dictionary, but somehow the definition didn't do it justice. Deep inside, Kizzy felt that the word meant so much more and was beyond anything that mere words could express. She wondered if God really needed to rest. Probably not, but with a shrinking feeling she recalled when she had finished something, like mowing the yard, she always sat back and relaxed, looking at how nice it was. Is that why God rested? To enjoy the beauty of His Creation? Look at it now, Kizzy thought. What a mess we've made of things. Even on the Sabbath.

5. "Honour your parents." At this point in time this seemed to be a useless effort. Both of her parents were dead to the world. He father had died

when she was ten. She knew little about honoring and respecting. Mostly because it hadn't been taught to her in clear words and actions. Her mother had been a tad bit abusive. She hadn't much liked her mother when she was alive. Now it was too late. In hindsight, Kizzy wished it had all been different. Was there hope of forgiveness? Yes, she believed there was. With the Grace provided by Jesus and the true remorse she felt, there was hope. She could honor and respect her parents after their deaths. She loved them and prayed for forgiveness. Plus, she could honor all those who were elderly and there WAS her Eternal Father. How much He deserved it. How very much.

6. "Don't kill." Well…so much for this one too. At the age of about 23, Kiz had found herself pregnant. It was only natural for her to seek an abortion. She had given no thought at all to the fact that it was a child, a blessing from God. In her drug-enhanced drunken stupor, it seemed like the thing to do. As she found out later, it wasn't. It was wrong. When someone mentioned abortion, she felt her emotions rise. They would say it was a choice, not a child. Bullpucky. When was the last time someone you know gave birth to a toaster? It was always a child. It was life. It was a human life. And it was given no chance whatsoever. Abortion was murder. It was human sacrifice. An abomination to our Creator. Which idols did that serve? Ego? Selfishness? Embarrassment? Kiz searched herself but couldn't find an answer for what she had done. She had been in deep darkness and that's all she could come up with. The influence of evil was very real and palpable. The blindness clouded everything. All Kizzy knew was that she was sad and very, very sorry.

8. "Don't steal." Long time ago. Been there, done that. Never again.

9. Hmm…Kiz always thought this simply said "Thou shall not lie." It didn't. Thou shalt not bear false witness against thy neighbor. She knew that "… *all liars, shall know their part in the lake which burneth with fire and brimstone: which is the second death." In Revelation 21:8.* She decided lying was lying, no matter who or what it was about. She didn't lie on purpose anymore, but sometimes things slipped out by accident. She supposed they counted, too. Part of this was due to the fact that her memory wasn't what it used to be. So Kizzy took great pains to make sure she was never late and that

she did what she said she would do. It upset her when people didn't do what they said. Maybe upset wasn't the right word, she was more disappointed for them than anything else. She remembered many times she had waited somewhere for a Christian brother or sister who never showed up at all. Most of the time she only got a vague excuse from them. And never an apology. Something came up, I forgot, I couldn't make it. Some, Kizzy had stopped making plans with altogether. If you couldn't believe a Christian, who could you believe? There was always forgiveness though. Kiz knew that back in her old-self days there were plenty of times when she didn't show up. She tried to keep a New Testament story in her mind as a deterrent to not doing what she said. Ananias and Sapphira. They were believers and were struck dead in an instant for a lie and deception. So then, are we to believe they were immediately translated into the presence of God? What happened to them? Where did they go? What does God do with a believer who deliberately lies, is flippant about keeping dates and appointments and doesn't keep their word? Kizzy didn't want to find out.

10. "Do not covet." Wanting what other people had was never really a problem for her. She never tried to "keep up with the Jones's." Things didn't hold that much attraction. But she knew people that did have that problem and it usually ended pretty badly. She thought she was generally content with what the Good Lord had so graciously given her. But there were some things that she couldn't easily recall. She didn't want to dig deep. Maybe let sleeping dogs lie. She was sure she was guilty of this somehow, sometime, somewhere, but at present it wasn't a problem.

"behold, all things are become new."
In 2 Corinthians 5:17

This was part of the shock that Kizzy was so sure threatened her sanity that summer. New not always means good or better. She began to realize that most of the faith, trust and hope that should have been in God were placed in other things. Worldly things.

She knew she was nuts. She had to be. But the Lord was with her and saw her through it. Kizzy had tried talking to some friends about her new condition, but they also informed her she was crazy, off the wall. It seemed that Christians had become so deeply entrenched in the world that the Truth was foreign to them. It wasn't the Truth, it was a lie. Was she trying to start some kind of cult or something? What is wrong with you?

> *"But now, O Lord, Thou art our Father, we are the clay,*
> *and Thou our Potter;*
> *and we all are the Work of Thy Hand."*
> Isaiah 64:8

> *"Hath not the Potter Power over the clay,"*
> In Romans 9:21

Kizzy likened the process to cleaning out the house of an elderly person who had fallen asleep in the Lord. As the precious gifts of illumination and enlightenment grew, it was like throwing open the heavy curtains in that elderly person's home. What looked okay in the gloom, on closer inspection, was not okay. There was filth and clutter that the person absolutely was not able to take care of.

Rooms that hadn't been touched in years. Some items only needed to be cleaned up and they were fine, fit for use. Other things had become so soiled and perverted that there was only one choice - throw them away. A few things weren't any longer what they started out to be. And as you clean, you find a great many parts and pieces that don't fit in anywhere. They don't belong.

Kiz used this method, with the Lord's guidance of course, to sort out, inspect and clean everything that touched her life. Some Christians told her "all things in moderation," but she rejected that immediately. A little boozing, a little gambling, a little fornication, a little soft porn and we were just like the "good people" of the secular world. It wasn't going to work for her.

She believed that the Potter molded the clay from birth to death. Some people appeared to be more easily reshaped than others, more open to the reworking of the Potter's ways.

Kiz had been in different shoes in times past. She wondered what had been the turning point in her thinking. She had been one of those Christians who were at a stalemate. Believing they were just fine in their walk with Jesus and refusing to be molded any further. They were in a spiritual rut and were content to stay there. Not Kizzy anymore. Now that the refining had begun, she didn't want to miss a moment of it. What did the Lord have in store for the rest of her life? She wanted to know.

As Kizzy sorted through the mess that her life had become, she wanted to make sure it didn't go back to what it had been. Not wanting to dwell on evil TOO much, she decided she needed to find out exactly what she was up against. She knew what she didn't want in her life anymore, but how could she avoid backsliding? Kiz had somehow reached the point in her life where she wanted God to receive all of the Glory that He so richly deserved.

Chapter 2

"For we wrestle not against flesh and blood, but against princi-
palities, against powers, against the rulers of the darkness of this
world, against spiritual wickedness in high places."
Ephesians 6:12

This sounded ominous. If we weren't physically wrestling with evil, it must all be in our heads. Or was it? Kizzy recalled physical accounts in the Bible as well. Must we use everything the Good Lord gave us plus He Himself to fight this battle? She was sure of it. How easy it was to just let things slip by, not giving them any thought whatsoever. Was that our first mistake? Not thinking? Dismissing too many things too easily?

That and completely ignoring the Word and Way of God. Principalities? Rulers? Darkness? Powers? Spiritual wickedness? These all sounded like they had great strength. Was she strong enough to handle it? Did she need to be? God was All Powerful. Satan was nothing in comparison.

"Now the serpent was more subtil than any beast of the field
which the Lord God had made."
Genesis 3:1

When she looked up the word subtle, red lights flashed. Webster's: mentally keen, delicately skillful, crafty, not obvious. No wonder Eve was so easily tricked; no wonder there were so many people being tricked. Brainwashed, deceived, whatever you wanted to call it. The deception wasn't forced. It was never forced.

Sin and the result of it were very ugly indeed. But they always came wrapped in beautiful, intriguing, mysterious, glittering, magical packages. The old saying, "curiosity killed the cat," came into Kizzy's mind. We go willingly.

Like the kid who thinks a few beers won't hurt and ends up later in life with cirrhosis of the liver, enlarged organs, dehydration, tumors, and tremors. The devil sneaks into any little crack he can find, then kicks the door wide open. The best have been swallowed up by him.

"Behold, all that he hath is in thy power."
In Job 1:12

Kizzy shuddered. God had given permission to the devil to do whatever he wished with all that Job had. God admitted that Satan had power. God had given him that power. Kiz wondered if it was safe to say that until the Lord had the last Word, nothing good was going to come of this.

If God let the devil have control over the life of a perfect and upright man like Job, are we being egotistical to think that He would never allow such a thing in our lives? Kizzy looked back over the events of her life. It was possible and more along the lines of Truth, it was probable that such things were still happening.

"The oxen were plowing, and the asses feeding beside them:
and the Sabeans fell upon them, and took them away;
yea, they have slain the servants with the edge of the sword;
and I only am escaped alone to tell thee."
Job 1:14,15

Hmm…what did she see here? Obviously Satan had the power to control the minds of the masses. How else would the Sabeans be of one mind to do what they did at that particular time? Control the minds of whole nations or tribes. That explained a lot about what Kizzy had been noticing lately. Contrary to what she had been told, Satan COULD take lives, kill people or have them killed. It was right there: slain the servants. This was serious business. A wave of panic crept through her as she wondered if the Sabeans thought they made the decision by themselves and were in control of their actions.

The fire of God is fallen from Heaven, and hath burned up the
sheep, and the servants, and consumed them;"
In Job 1:16

What could fire from Heaven possibly be? Kiz wondered. Whatever it was, the devil had control over it. The fire didn't just kill the sheep and servants, it consumed them. Kiz pictured flat, smoldering piles of ashes.

"The Chaldeans made out three bands, and fell upon the camels,
and have carried them away, yea,
and slain the servants with the edge of the sword."
In Job 1:17

More massive mind control over a different nation or tribe. She wasn't exactly sure what the Chaldeans were. More theft. More murder. If it had happened twice in one day, couldn't it still continue to happen? Like in the minds of Americans, or Mexicans or Canadians? Kizzy was sure, but no one would believe her. We do have free will, you know. We are too smart for that. And we are being guided and protected by God, remember? Kiz wasn't completely convinced.

"Thy sons and thy daughters were eating and drinking wine in
their eldest brother's house: And, behold, there came a great wind
from the wilderness, and smote the four corners of the house, and
it fell upon the young men, and they are dead;"
In Job 1:18,19

So, she thought, he can also control the weather. What was there in the world, (or spiritual world, too, for that matter,) that he couldn't control? Besides the Holy Trinity, of course. If other people's minds could be controlled, hers could be too. Could all of these events in Job's life so far be called "an act of God?" She supposed they could be, because God created all things and allowed the devil to have power over them. She knew Satan was on a short leash, but he sure seemed to be able to cause an awful lot of trouble anyhow.

"So Satan went forth from the presence of the Lord, and smote
Job with sore boils from the sole of his foot unto his crown."
Job 2:7

Here it was obvious to Kiz that the devil could afflict us with illness if God so allowed it. Was there no limit to his power? Oh, yes, God set limits to what he had to abide by, but beyond that, how powerful was Satan? How much damage would the Lord really let him do?

"Then entered Satan into Judas surnamed Iscariot."
In Luke 22:3

Kizzy shuddered again. If Satan enters into you, does that mean you are damned? He could actually enter into people. She recalled the legion that was sent into the swine. The man was healed, but did the evil spirits drown with the pigs or were they trapped in the dead pigs' bodies? What about when they decayed to nothing? Did they escape to invade someone else? Kiz was pretty sure that the spirits existed forever.

There is so much the Bible doesn't tell us, but are these omissions important? The fact is, Satan can, will and probably still does enter people. That power was scarier to her than the rest.

"Then was Jesus led up of the Spirit into the wilderness
to be tempted of the devil."
Matthew 4:1

"Then the devil taketh Him up into the Holy City,
and setteth Him on a pinnacle of the temple."
Matthew 4:5

"Again, the devil taketh Him up to an exceeding high mountain,
and sheweth Him all the kingdoms of the world,
and the glory of them;"
Matthew 4:8

The devil had the power to "take" Jesus? God! The Son of God! He actually took Him? We are way weaker and it would be very easy for Satan to take us. How did Jesus respond to all of this temptation? And He WAS tempted. Kizzy contemplated the word. Tempted.

Jesus responded with the Word of God. Scripture. It was probably easy for Him to do. He (They) dictated It to the Holy, Righteous men of God. What about us? Most of us are so wrapped up in the world that we take very little time, more like none at all, to read the Word, let alone study it thoroughly. So if we only read and understand a little bit, that provides a very small arsenal of weapons to use against the evil one.

> *"But the Comforter, which is the Holy Ghost,*
> *Whom the Father will send in My Name,*
> *He shall teach you all things, And bring*
> *all things to your remembrance,*
> *whatsoever I Have said unto You."*
> *John 14:26*

Kizzy decided it was time to get crackin'! If the Word was sharper than any two-edged sword, she best arm herself well if she had any hope at all of winning the battle. God had given Satan varied powers, maybe a lot more than these few verses stated. She knew the battle was the Lord's; she also knew that He always asked you to do your part. Even if it was just to wait for movement in the tops of the mulberry trees.

> *"Let the Word of Christ dwell in you richly."*
> *Colossians 3:16*

As Kizzy worked, that's what she did. Someone had told her she was in a dark place and needed to dwell on the good. As much as she would like to, she knew the Lord was teaching her something important. We were to learn from every Word that was in the Bible. It was all the Word of Christ because:

> *"All things were made by Him; and without Him*
> *was not any thing made that was made."*
> *John 1:3*

Even the dark parts of it. We needed to know ALL of the Truth. Not just the "good" stuff. A man she had once spoken with had likened reading the Scripture to putting a tea bag in water. Sooner or later something was going to happen. God had put His people in dark places before and she was confident that when it was His Good Time, He would bring her out of it.

Her tea bag may be steeping in a dark place, but something was happening. She could still see the Light and she loved that Light dearly. Her trust was in Jesus on this matter.

Her train of thought went over all the powers she knew Satan had and ways to avoid being tricked or snared. His ways led to only one place. Hell. That was one thing she had never heard in a sermon. And to her, it was extremely important. She'd heard lots of other things in sermons, but those were for other chapters. Hell. The place where disobedient, filthy, unholy sinners were sent for all eternity.

Torture, torment, pain, suffering, loneliness, thirst, regret, lostness, bleakness, darkness. No thought of any kind of hope. EVER! If these kinds of things were never discussed, how could anyone even begin to understand the importance of what Jesus had done for us? How could it make the least little difference in an unbeliever's life? How were people to know what the consequences of their sins were?

No one talked about it. It became taboo to speak of it. You were getting into things that were none of your business. You were being judgmental and that was a no-no. It was probably even in man's laws somewhere. Was it hate speech to tell someone they were going to Hell? Probably. Who wanted to be politically incorrect anyhow?

It was what Kizzy began calling the "quieting." Satan's delicately skillful, evil, power and control over the world was causing everyone to become passive. Lukewarm. Fear was a big factor, too. "Don't judge lest ye be judged." There was a really big difference to her between being judgmental and telling the truth. But nobody wanted to hear it, or say it. Christians were supposed to live in peace. End of story.

S.S. Riley

So…all of the sermons she heard were about peace, love, forgiveness, tolerance and acceptance. No one wanted a controversy and no one wanted to insult anyone. Yes, Satan's quieting was pretty much successful. Take away the truth and all that's left is lies. Kizzy didn't like or understand much of what she saw or heard in Churches, so she chalked it up to deception. Hers or theirs?

With Christians passively under his control, Satan was free to do whatever he wanted. Under the Lord God's watchful Eye and as far as his leash would go, of course. It seemed his biggest desire, his keenest intent, was to pollute and defile God's greatest creation: man. And as long as man didn't mind, the going was easy. Man was doing a pretty good job of it all by himself.

Also in his evil jealousy and greed, Satan was hell-bent on polluting and destroying all God made that was "good." Man was happily helping with that one, too. With what little wisdom and knowledge the Good Lord had seen befitting to lay on Kizzy, she saw that Satan's plan was going along just fine.

When she tried to talk to other Christians about the meatier parts of the Bible, things didn't go so well, she was shut down. One friend in her seventies is a walking companion. Taking a trail at a nearby park in early autumn, the scenery was gorgeous.

Talk centered around her friend's upcoming surgery, travel plans, grandkids in school, etc. At a quiet break in the conversation, Kiz had clearly and lovingly praised God for giving them so many beautiful things to look at, to proclaim His Awesome Glory. She had received a questioning sideways glance, no comment was made and the conversation quickly returned to the things of the world.

With another Christian friend, Kiz had tried to get into the Word. She didn't recall the topic but was flatly told that the friend chose to steer clear of such things and think nice, happy thoughts. That conversation ended up floating around on top of worldly things but lacked sincerity for Christ.

Kizzy wondered later how many Christians were happy sipping at the milk, unwilling to take a big bite and chew it slowly. She wondered too if there had been much spiritual growth in their lives. Some had been of the faith their entire lives and still stumbled over some of the simpler names like Isaiah and

Ezekiel. She prayed for them. No judgment on her part, she was just trying to figure out whether you could be transformed if you were pretty much completely conformed to the ways of the world. Only God knew for sure.

One consolation she had was an elderly gentleman in his eighties. He would share his concerns and talk of Biblical things with her. In her world, if it wasn't for him, she might have renamed the quieting, the silencing.

Chapter 3

"And be not conformed to this world."
In Romans 12:2

Kiz prayed and asked God what things we shouldn't be conformed to. This was part of her paralyzing. It was too late. Even the most devout Christians had fallen. And now what? What was God going to do with us unbelieving, disobedient, conformed to the world people? All of us who said we were Christians but were blinded? Was it our fault? Had we let our ears become deaf, our eyes become blind, our minds become void of understanding and our hearts become hardened?

"Because strait is the gate, and narrow is the way,
which leadeth unto life, and few there be that find it."
Matthew 7:14

"for wide is the gate, and broad is the way, that leadeth
to destruction, and many there be which go in thereat:"
Matthew 7:13

What was the narrow way? Kizzy thought long and hard. She knew Jesus was the only way to salvation through His Grace, but it had to be more than that. Repentance was a big thing. If His Grace was all that mattered, Paul wouldn't have written so many letters to straighten people out. Not once could she recall him saying that this or that behavior was okay because Jesus' Grace would wipe it all away.

She decided it had to be your total package. Everything was right there in the Bible. But who was serious about that old thing anymore? She had once read a Church sign that said: "Our religion may be 2000 years old, but our thinking isn't." Had they wandered from the narrow way?

The wide gate had to be the world. So the narrow way had to be away from the world. It was time to start getting off the treadmill; one or two steps at a time. The Lord had laid it on her heart to figure it out. She didn't want to think about what would happen if she didn't. It felt much more like a Command than a passing thought. It was going to happen. Her life was going to become as narrow as she could possibly get it.

"Ye cannot serve God and mammon."
In Luke 16:13

That's what had been happening. She was serving the world. We all were. We had become slaves to it, to money. Did that mean we couldn't be serving God? We had jumped on every single bandwagon that came along. And we were paying for it. Every cent from our pockets, working overtime, two jobs, second mortgages, loans, credit cards. We were running ourselves ragged for the world, for money, for the evil one. Why?

Kizzy felt sick to her stomach. Did our paying go much deeper? Into things we couldn't see? We were set in our ways, up with the times, fulfilling our every whim and desire. And NOTHING was going to change us. But...would we end up paying with our souls?

"And having food and raiment let us therewith be content."
1 Timothy 6:8

It had gone way beyond that. We really weren't content with anything. There was very little contentment, least of all with our Lord and Savior. We all wanted more, more, more. Our monthly bills showed that. They kept getting higher and higher. More. We needed more. More of everything. Gimmee,

gimmee, gimmee. Me, me, me. It was all about us and what we wanted. None of it was about God. Didn't we understand what "covet" meant? Or does all that stuff apply to everyone else and not us?

We prayed that God would give us more and when He didn't or took something away, we demanded to know why. We would go after it ourselves, we would find a way to get it. We couldn't live without our stuff. No, the truth was, we refused to live without our stuff. More stuff. And more stuff. We never had enough.

Yes, Kizzy could see it as plain as the nose on her face. We were so conformed to the world that she couldn't really see any way out. It was going to take the Wisdom of God to make a difference.

> *"If the world hate you, ye know that it hated Me before*
> *it hated you."*
> *John 15:18*

Yes, Kizzy felt the dawning of earthly despair. We had all become the dreaded Pharisees. Yet it had to be done. Playing around in candy land was over. She had to try to make them see, but how could she? She would become a laughing-stock and ridiculed. Maybe even stoned or beheaded. Some would believe and repent. Most wouldn't. Sin was for somebody else, not me. I'm doing what I'm supposed to do.

Kiz put her head in her hands as the craziness swirled around in her brain. Yes, she was nuts. All these years of deep thinking had landed her in a very precarious position, worldly speaking. The weight of the world was heavy on her shoulders.

Yes, God, here I am. Use me. I love you.

Chapter 4

"not to think of himself more highly than he ought to think."
In Romans 12:3

But we do.

Since she had been told that man was God's greatest creation, it seemed only logical for Kiz to start there. How had God created us to be? Then the thought hit her. The way we were without any help from man. Natural. Yeah, Lord, like that was going to fly in this world! But she had to try.

One of the biggest idols we were worshipping was our bodies. A love/hate relationship. We cared more about what other people thought than what God thought. Since we were worshipping self, that made many areas of our lives perverse, but Kiz was looking at the body first. She would tackle other areas later. The body was important, yes, but how important? Was it all-important? No. Kizzy was now seeing it as a caterpillar of sorts. It was an incubator for the soul. That was the important part. What was beauty in God's eyes?

"for ye are like unto whited sepulchres, which indeed
appear beautiful outward, but are within full of dead men's
bones, and of all uncleanness."
In Matthew 23:27

"God shall smite thee, thou whited walls:"
In Acts 23:3

Hadn't we learned anything in over 2000 years of being Christians? Beauty to God was the state of the soul, not the package it came in. But the "world" had lots of things to sell and they couldn't very well do it without advertising could they? People were sucked in by it. The ego and self worship had made beauty a must have. No matter what the cost. And it was expensive.

Kizzy started watching ads with her eyes wide open, seeing every detail, every putdown, every temptation and listening to every word. People were suffering because they couldn't fit into what the world said was beautiful. But they were still whiting their walls the best they could. Why couldn't we just let it go?

Because the world expected, no, demanded it. But God didn't. God abhorred it. It was destruction of inner peace on a grand scale. Not many caterpillars were all that great looking, but they rested and were transformed into beautiful creatures that flew away. Kizzy wondered where her soul would fly away to.

"Ye are of your father the devil, and the lusts of your father
ye will do. He was a murderer from the beginning,
and abode not in the truth, because there is no truth in him.
When he speaketh a lie, he speaketh of his own:
for he is a liar, and the father of it."
John 8:44

"and all liars shall have their part in the lake that
burneth with fire and brimstone: which is the second death."
In Revelation 21:8

"Blessed is the man unto whom the Lord imputeth
not iniquity, and in whose spirit there is no guile."
Psalm 32:2

Kizzy may have taken some things out of context, but as the Light shone ever brighter, all of the Word had taken on much greater importance. Lies were not all verbal and the result of those silent lies was as disastrous as the result

S.S. Riley

of the spoken ones. Any sort of deception was a lie. With Satan's help we had become ashamed of the way we looked, how we appeared in other people's eyes. The perfect design with which the Lord had created us in the image of God, yet we feared what others thought of the way we looked.

How much of a slap in the face was that to our Creator? You didn't do a good enough job! I am going to fix all of the things You did wrong about me! I know better than you!

Yes, wasn't ego one of the seven deadly sins? Was that even Biblical? We were sure doing that one up and good. What did we covet about someone else's appearance that made us crazy enough to go for it? Kiz decided she wanted no guile in her and watched for places where it needed to be eradicated.

> *"But if a woman have long hair, it is a glory to her; for her*
> *hair is given her for a covering."*
> *1 Corinthians 11:15*

> *"Judge in yourselves: is it comely*
> *that a woman pray to God uncovered?"*
> *1 Corinthians 11:13*

So...start at the top she did. She let her dyed hair grow out for one full year to the day. Then she had all of the lie cut off. She washed it and kept it brushed, but other than that, did nothing to it.

> *"Whose adorning let it not be the outward adorning*
> *of plaiting the hair,"*
> *1 Peter 3:3*

Everything went in the trash. Curling irons, straightening irons, dye, hairspray, clips, barrettes, all of it that had to do with hair. That expense was gone. At this point in time, her hair was well past her shoulders and streaked with gray. She didn't care. It was actually a relief, a burden lifted from her. She realized she didn't really care what the world thought anymore. It was the hair her Creator God had given her. She hoped at least that part of her was now on the narrow path. Yikes! There was so much else to look at.

"for whom thou didst wash thyself, paintedst thy eyes, and
deckedst thyself with ornaments."
Ezekiel 23:40

"For all that is in the world, the lust of the flesh, and the
lust of the eyes, and the pride of life, is
not of the Father, but is of the world."
1 John 2:16

Okay. Kizzy was getting serious. More stuff went into the trash. "Hey! That's a lot of money you're throwing away there! You shouldn't be doing that! It's a sin. It's a waste." Satan taunted her.

No! If I end up in Hell with you for deception, tortured and tormented for all eternity, that's the waste.

It was done. It was over.

Makeup, eye shadow, eyeliner, wrinkle cream, eyelash curler, all of it…gone. Somewhere Kiz had heard that our skin was the largest organ of the body. It absorbed everything that was put on it. This was proven to her by patches. Nicotine patch, pain patch, birth control patch, car sickness patch.

All these chemicals in all this stuff, doing ,God only knows, what to us. Well, Satan knew, that was part of his plan. Pollute and destroy what God had so lovingly made.

And people wondered why they were sick all the time. Where were those diseases and all of this sickness and cancer coming from? Take a guess. Open your eyes and THINK for a change. We are doing it to ourselves with all of this, this STUFF. All of it went into the trash. Everything designed to go on the skin. Gone.

"Also he shall wash his flesh in water, and he shall be clean."
Leviticus 14:9

S.S. Riley

"Thus saith the Lord, The heaven is MY Throne, and
the earth is My Footstool:"
In Isaiah 66:1

"and shouldest destroy them which destroy the earth."
In Revelation 11:18

Wash with water and you will be clean. Was there a reason for that statement? Of course. Should we bother to find out what that reason was? Or just take God at His Word.

So where had all of this other stuff come from? And why did we believe it was a good thing? The body wash, the germ killer, hand sanitizer, facial cleanser, hand soap, shampoo, conditioner. Oh yeah, from the world! Not only did Satan push the all important beauty, he pushed the have to smell good, too. And fear.

Weren't we destroyers of the earth? Would we be destroyed? We would do and use anything to attain the goals set by our idols. Every single thing we sent down the drain went into our water supply. Combined with all of the stuff everyone else uses, it added up to a lot. God's footstool was being polluted in a major way and yes, we were all guilty. If water was good enough for God, it had to be good enough for Kiz. More crap went into the trash. Never to be bought again.

What else was deception that was used on the body? The Lord made us to smell a certain way. Bye-bye deodorant. De odor ant. Stop the body from doing what it was designed to do. Make the Lord's Work gross. Pondering the laws of nature that the Lord had put into place, bad smells were a fact of life. Air fresheners gone. Saying there weren't any bad smells was a lie. Besides, breathing those chemical fumes probably caused lung cancer.

Kizzy tried, in her pitiful human mind, to imagine perfume being absorbed into her body. How did it affect the areas it reached? Muscle, tissue, blood? Besides giving her a headache, was it causing adverse effects on her health?

Breast cancer? The world tried to deny that all of those chemicals in deodorant played a part in it, but Kizzy wasn't convinced. Even men were getting breast cancer. Enough was enough. She would smell the way God intended for her to smell and if the world didn't like it, they could lump it.

Now her mind was fast forwarding. What else did she need to get rid of to get closer to the narrow path? If God hadn't wanted hair in certain places He wouldn't have put it there. Razors hit the trash can. Kiz examined every single personal item she owned. She didn't like what the implications were. Her vanity sickened her.

It wasn't long before the world started to notice.

Do something with yourself!

I am. I'm trying to find the narrow way and develop a closer walk with my Lord, Creator and Savior, but the world keeps getting in the way.

I need to keep myself attractive for my husband, there's a lot of competition out there.

Well then, maybe you and your husband both need to find out what marriage is in God's eyes.

I have to look good for work.

Hmmm…maybe if you didn't demand so much worldly stuff, you wouldn't need to work. Your husband does have a good income, you know.

Kizzy tried to keep in mind that all of the comments, insults and helpful suggestions were coming from the world. She ignored them. In all honesty it was the voice of her God she was listening for, not the voice of the world.

Chapter 5

"God created"
In Genesis 1:1

Don't you think that with the line of work you're in that maybe you should start thinking differently about these things?

What does being a home repair specialist have to do with anything?

If what you say you believe is true, why bother?

What are you talking about? Most of the time you make no sense at all.

The way you think it should make all the sense in the world.

How so? I know you aren't going to shut up about this until you make your point, so please do it.

What are you working on right now?

Repairing a curved stairway that's been neglected for decades.

So, starting with the basics, what's the first thing you know?

That I'm repairing a curved stairway that's been neglected for decades.

Go back further.

Repairing a curved stairway someone else built that's been neglected for decades.

Farther back.

What? The need for a stairway to begin with?

Further.

What do you mean?

Think about the laws that were put in place when God created the world.

God didn't create the world.

That's the myth I'm trying to debunk because if you don't change your way of thinking, you'll end up in hell.

That's a myth too. When you die, you're just dead.

So you say. All that happens in life means nothing? I doubt that. So…in your opinion, what laws just happened to accidentally evolve?

I have no idea what you're talking about.

Why don't you just sit down and wait? Watch and see the stairway evolve into exactly what the client wants.

It doesn't work that way and you know it.

We're making headway! So what law do you think applies here?

Does this really involve some kind of law?

Of course. Now think hard.

I'm drawing a blank.

Maybe the law that says if someone doesn't do it, it doesn't get done? If someone doesn't put it there, there's nothing there?

That's true. But it isn't a law. It's more like a fact. Conjecture maybe.

How can it be conjecture if you just said it's true?

You know what I mean.

No, that's the sad part. If I knew every thought, feeling, nuance and emotion behind every word that was said, I'd be God.

But there is no....

Yes, there is. And He put rules into place. What rule did we just go over?

If someone doesn't do it, it doesn't get done. Someone has to put it there.

Right. So with this rule in mind, what do you need to repair the curved stairway?

There's so much, do I need to name it all?

What's the one basic thing you cannot do the job without?

But I need it all.

No, that's not what I'm getting at. Think. If you didn't have what, you couldn't even begin to think about doing it.

A brain?

No silly, get down to basics. Think.

I don't know what you mean.

What are the steps made of?

Oh, I see. Lumber. Yes, the answer would be wood.

Fantastic. What kind of wood?

Oak. It's really expensive.

What is a cheaper wood?

I'd have to say pine.

Then why don't you use pine and wait for it to evolve into oak?

It doesn't work that way. I already told you that.

Isn't it your belief that everything just accidentally happened? Stuff just became stuff to exist? Now you tell me it doesn't work that way? You don't sound very convincing. You better do some work on your game plan.

Oak is oak and pine is pine. They have different qualities.

If they both evolved from exactly the same thing, how can they have different qualities?

I don't know.

Why don't you work on crossing an oak with a pine? Then you could have cheaper expensive wood.

That won't work. It just won't.

So you're admitting there's another law at work here.

Maybe. I hadn't thought about it. What law is that?

Things can only be what they are unless man interferes with his evil, mad science.

Probably.

So you believe that some kind of amoeba crawled out of a soupy, swampy mess and became an oak tree or a pine tree?

Something like that. It's complicated.

It most certainly is and it raises all kinds of questions.

Don't get started.

I'm already started and you're going to finish. Where did this soupy, swampy mess with amoebas in it come from? And don't try to get off easy by saying it was there.

I regress.

To late. That's the trouble with you guys.

What guys? Me guys? Where's the problem?

You make statements about your beliefs, but you have no real answers to back them up. Pretty flimsy beliefs if you ask me.

Who asked you? People have told me you are nuts, now I'm beginning to believe them.

Believe what you want, but I want answers. Where did the amoebas in the soupy, swampy mess come from?

I have no idea.

That's right, you don't. So the second law we discussed still applies here. Things can only be what they are.

I guess.

Where did the amoebas get life? How did they know what to become? Did one just say to itself, I'll become an oak tree, you be a pine tree? Don't you think that an amoeba can multiply billions and billions of times but it's divisions will still only be amoebas?

I don't know.

Where did they get the knowledge that they would have to adapt to different seasons and climates if they were going to survive? How did they process the information about their surroundings? How do they know when to start producing leaves and seeds? How do they know how long they have to do these things before they need to go dormant and prepare for winter? How do they place life in their seeds?

I don't know.

I do. Someone gave them that knowledge. It isn't possible for even the most intelligent human to do that. Maybe you should start asking yourself some serious questions. What was your occupation before you started working on houses?

You know good and well that I was a landscaper. What is wrong with you?

Just making a point is all. How many kinds of plants would you say you worked with over the years?

Hundreds.

Kinds of plants?

Yes. Hundreds.

So you're asking me to believe that an army of amoebas marched out of the swamp and all decided to become different plants? Under the exact same conditions? Plus each one figured out all by itself how to make more of the same plants they had accidentally evolved into?

S.S. Riley

I don't know. I'm not asking you to believe anything.

I can see why. Why don't they keep evolving?

Maybe they do.

Come on. Grapes have been grapes for thousands of years. What else can they evolve into? Do they have a "stop evolving" button somewhere? Where did they get that?

I don't know. For crying out loud, are you almost finished?

Maybe. You aren't denying that there is a lot you don't know and a lot you can't see. Things you will never know and never see?

No, I'm not denying it. Nobody knows it all. Not even you.

That's right. I don't know it all, but I think. Obviously you believe something you aren't convinced of yourself. How are you going to convince anyone else?

I'm not going to try.

I see. I have one more question.

Go for it.

If someone else put it here, as we earlier agreed they did, does that make it theirs? Are we thieves by taking it and making it our own?

That's two questions and I'm not answering either one.

Because you don't know the answers.

Precisely.

Chapter 6

The first Church Kizzy seriously attended was very large and very beautiful. She loved being there. Just being in a Holy Place, as she considered it, did wonders for her soul. The building was huge, but the congregation was small. She sometimes, at first, wondered why.

Kiz volunteered for many things, the biggest being a community breakfast before services on Sunday. A lot of people came to eat, but very few stayed afterwards. It all started out as pure joy to serve the Lord, but over a period of eighteen months it turned into a time of grieving.

There were times during the services when her skin began to crawl. Nothing exactly that she could put her finger on firmly. More like inferences. Things implied but not said directly.

Like the one sermon where she discerned the pastor wanted Glenn Beck to burn in hell for all eternity. No, he never came right out and said it, but it felt like it to Kiz, that's what it was all adding up to. Kizzy liked Mr. Beck and agreed with a lot of what he said.

After awhile, she discovered that the pulpit was being used to further political agendas. The pastor must have been having a particularly good day when he went into a fit, shouting he was sick and tired of everyone and their petty problems. HE only wanted Annas and Ezekiels in HIS church. If you weren't an Anna or an Ezekiel, you could hit the road and never come back. HE would be glad about it and the Church would be better for it. Kiz was shocked. No wonder the congregation was so small. But she stayed. She prayed the Lord would show her the beam in her own eye.

Kiz was shocked again when she asked to lead a Bible study. There wasn't one in the Church. The pastor told her he really didn't want one because some things in there might be offensive to part of the congregation.

A study had to be approved by him and he would see what he could come up with. Nothing was ever done about it.

One member of the board asked if there would be anyone else helping to lead the study if there was one because it would take a very highly educated person to teach HER anything. Kizzy was so sad that she cried. To think you knew so much, thought only of yourself and refused to participate in fellowship and instruction of the younger women. She wanted to point that out to the board member, but somehow she knew it would be futile. She kept her mouth shut. There was no Bible study.

Kiz remembered vividly the day she lost all respect for the pastor. She and another person were attending the required classes to become members of the Church.

The pastor started looking for something. Opening drawers and cupboards. Then he said that when he first came to the Church the congregation was nothing but a bunch of "white hairs." He was looking for a picture of them. He couldn't find the picture but said someone had written on it: try to find two under seventy-five. Then he said two arrows had been drawn on it pointing to two people they thought MIGHT be under seventy-five.

He was chuckling when he said they contributed nothing to the Church and were just sitting around waiting to die. There was a gleam in his eye when he said he was glad the worthless bums had finally been run off.

Kiz felt indignation and fury as she had never known it before. These people, the Body of Christ, had probably worked their whole lives serving their Lord. It was their tithes, offerings and sweat that had built, furnished and maintained HIS church for decades. They were faithful followers of Christ and he had driven them away. Plus, he was proud of the fact, bragging about it.

In retrospect, Kizzy couldn't figure out why she had kept her mouth shut. Maybe it was the shock of hearing something like that. She wished later she had unleashed the full fury of her emotions on him. Again, she prayed for the Lord to show her the beam in her own eye.

There were many other things about the Church that left her with a sick, helpless feeling. A part-time administrator, friend of the preacher's, that raked in a whopping $60,000.00 a year. The fact that a position had been created for the preacher's son. She never knew how much he was paid but Kiz was sure it was a lot. A fulltime food service worker. A large staff that seemed to serve no purpose whatsoever.

Ninety-five percent of the food in the pantry that was handed out to the community was years past expiration date, including frozen meat. The pastor's wife cussing like a drunken sailor, her words echoing in the hallways.

And the crowning glory. Sexually active gay and lesbian couples everywhere. Some were even in positions of power and authority throughout the Church. Kiz was of a mind again, she wasn't perfect and had a somewhat sinful past herself. But having only read the Bible and discerning what it was saying, deep in her gut she knew this was wrong.

Once, a woman invited her to a monthly fellowship meeting centered around a karaoke theme. She was hesitant but talked herself into it. At least it was fellowship with other Christians. Or so she thought.

The first few acts were okay. Then two teenage girls got up to do a duet. It turned out to be a love song they were singing to each other. Dancing, kissing and caressing as they sang. With wide-eyed shock Kiz turned to look at the woman who had invited her. She was clapping softly, tears of joy streaming down her face. "Isn't it beautiful," she whispered, "where else would this be allowed to happen?"

In a Church? Oh dear. Reading the Bible hadn't prepared her for anything of the sort. Did the woman who had invited her think this was a date? Kizzy made a quick exit well before the duet was over. She couldn't be a spectator and certainly didn't condone this type of behavior inside the House of God.

But she stayed at the Church with a dampened attitude. The last straw was when the preacher announced he was going to take out the pews and replace them with chairs so they could worship in different ways. Since over 120 "worthless whitehairs" had been run off, money was tight. Assets had been sold and the money squandered.

No one knew for sure how the chairs were going to be paid for, but they all of a sudden became a necessity. There was no discussion. Probably a line of credit would have to be opened. If that was the case, they could get several of the tall café type tables with the tall stools. Yes, a coffee shop atmosphere was a good idea.

Kiz was mortified. She thought that a serious worshipper of our Lord Jesus would be happy to do it on a stump. She loved the pews. They had been there as long as the Church had. Over a hundred years and were in perfect condition. Now they were going to be sold as yard sale items. What was happening? It looked like the devil and strong egos had been allowed to take over. Kiz became extremely uncomfortable with the whole Church business. There wasn't even a stab at integrity or righteousness anywhere she looked. With a heavy heart, a mixed bag of emotions, her nose burning and tears in her eyes, she listened for the last time as the beautiful oak and stained glass doors closed behind her.

Chapter 7

"and men of high degree are a lie."
In Psalms 62:9

"and exalted them of low degree."
In Luke 1:52

"let the brother of low degree rejoice in that
he is exalted."
James 1:9

Kizzy had pretty much always known that education was one of the big distractions that was being idolized. She truly believed it was important to know the basics to get along in life. But a lot of stuff they were teaching her in school seemed like nonsense, when the Great Commission was "go and preach," why should a mind be cluttered with the capitals of all 50 states and algebra? What practical use did these facts have anyhow?

She walked away from school in the 9th grade. She just wasn't interested and couldn't see a point to any of it. Not that she was going to go and preach, that was the farthest thing from her mind. She was after the things the world had to offer, but education wasn't one of them.

As her sincere prayers for whatever knowledge and understanding the Lord wanted her to have were being answered and she began seeing things in a different light, more and more things weighed heavily on her mind.

The Church she was attending at the time was trying to get an after-school program in place through grants. She knew the evil one had the power to deceive all people if he so chose to do it. As everyone was talking about the program and trying to jump through all of the hoops to get things done according to the rules, Kiz only saw them as puppets of the devil.

Not one word was ever heard about the Lord during these discussions and preparations. There was no prayer. It seemed like this after-school program was the most important thing in the world and was going to happen no matter what. It took precedence over everything else. God wasn't even in the equation.

As Kizzy watched the progress, the plan seemed to be more about serving the world, not the Lord. No one was going to listen to her, she could tell that from the time the gate opened. The after-school program was being coveted.

In her growing frustration with what seemed to be secular churches, she was prompted to get a notebook. She started writing private letters to vent her angst. She named the notebook "Rude and Obnoxious Letters to the Secular Church from a Very Highly Uneducated Woman."

The first letter she wrote went like this:

"It seems to me that the reason you are having such a hard time getting an after-school program set up in the Church is because maybe the Lord doesn't want one here? Have you ever thought about that? When you pray about it, if you pray about it, are you asking God to do your will and not asking what His might be? Remember our thoughts are foolishness to the Lord.

The Church is supposed to be a place of praise, worship and thanksgiving. It's not supposed to be a place where we help children succeed in a world that we aren't supposed to be a part of. All earthly success counts for nothing in the end. Then what? Isn't it supposed to be the purpose of the Church and Christians to spread the Gospel and make disciples? How is an after-school program going to do that? We are defeating our own purpose. Or have we lost that purpose amidst the things of this world.

Things aren't going YOUR way. There's one huge problem after another. People you have counted on have disappeared into the woodwork. Is the Lord trying to tell you something? Are we bothering to listen or are we bulldozing our way ahead regardless of the consequences?

Jesus didn't call out very many highly educated people. In fact, He didn't have much nice to say about them. The ones with an education that He did call left their professions behind when they answered His call.

Luke was a physician but there is not one single time in the Bible where he was called on to heal anyone using his profession. Matthew was a tax collector. He got up and went when Jesus called leaving his job behind. And he didn't go back.

Paul, one of the greatest conversion success stories of all time, was vastly educated. Yet, he used none of it after he was struck blind.

My son's girlfriend has a daughter who was eight during the 2012 election. She came home from school all excited because she got to vote in a mock election. I asked her who she voted for. She said Obama. I asked her why and her answer shocked me.

'I like school and if that other guy gets elected, he will shut the schools down. Obama is FOR schools, the other guy is against them.' She didn't even know what the other guy's name was. When I tried to explain to her this wasn't true, she became extremely agitated and cried. Yes, it IS true, they told us at school. Nothing would change her mind.

Do I hear anyone snickering? Must I remind you that once we are a member of Christ's Body, as it says in Galatians 3:28: "*There is neither Jew nor Greek; there is neither bond nor free; there is neither male nor female: for ye are all one in Christ Jesus.*" Worldly things are divisive.

Should that verse have been expanded to state that there is neither Republican nor Democrat nor Liberal nor Conservative nor Independent? Or do you think the point was clearly made as written? Such things should not be given place in a Christian environment. Or a Christian life for that matter. We belong to Christ.

Is applying for grants, (asking the "world" or "powers that be") to further worldly intentions such a good idea for a Church? If the Church gets government grants, it ceases to be a Church and becomes just another strangling arm of the government with all of it's regulations.

This is my Church, too. I strongly believe that our time, talents, resources and energy would be much better spent going in an entirely different direction. If there are after-school activities in the Church, they should be centered around discipleship, not furthering a child's abilities to understand lies and propaganda. Maybe the schools should be shut down.

None of the neighborhood parents who are pushing for this program attend this Church. They don't bring their kids. Where else are the children going to get any kind of spiritual foundation? Nowhere? Why don't we care? If they need help with reading, help them read Bible stories and scripture. If they need help with writing, help them write Bible stories and scripture.

The Word of God is Powerful. Why would a Church neglect to use it? There is teaching and then there is Teaching. Which are we, as Christians who are called OUT of the world, required to do?

For an after-school program as planned in it's present form, I vote NO!"

Yes, well, Kiz never made copies and gave them to Church members, but she did write out one copy and gave it to the new preacher that was coming in. He was known as a young man who was experienced at applying for grants. That's one of the reasons he was so desired as the new preacher. She was thanked for sharing her letter, but she doubted he took her seriously. She no longer attended that Church, or any other for that matter.

"Every man therefore that hath heard, and hath learned
of the Father, cometh unto Me."
In John 6:45

S.S. Riley

Had learned of the Father? Did that mean he had learned from the Father? Kiz wasn't sure, but as she had already established in her mind, Satan was crafty and knowledgeable in a vast way. Were we learning more "of" him than we were "of" the Father?

It seemed clear to her that the more distracted he could keep people and the more interested he could keep them in their distractions, the less time and inclination they would have to bless their Lord by doing His Will and studying His Word. Since one of the huge idols that was being worshipped was self, it was pretty easy to keep them indulging in their egos. While self-absorbed they were uninterested and disobedient to the Word.

As folks become all consumed with "I want and I need" it is really easy to forget about what God wants. Satan's influences are strong. Since we are to be in the world, but not of the world, of course that's where he wants us to be.

"for Satan himself is transformed into an angel of light."
In 2 Corinthians 11:14

Kiz watched out for charming people. She preferred plain and simple. If Satan could transform into an angel of light she didn't put anything past him. Not even using the small, still voice associated with God.

"for by thy sorceries were all nations deceived."
In Revelation 18:23

"And the devil that deceived them."
In Revelation 20:10

Kiz knew people were deceived. The Bible stated it and gave multiple warnings about it. She was one of them. That was why she was narrowing her way. This was part of the meltdown that year. How easy it had been for her to be deceived. So if one person listened to her it would be worth all of the dislike and unpopularity she was experiencing.

Kiz thought about the evils of education a lot. It took prayer, guidance and discernment to put it all together in an understandable order. Or was it understandable or in any kind of order? That was another part of her dilemma. She wasn't sure.

"But the tree of knowledge of good and evil, thou
shalt not eat of it."
In Genesis 2:17

Plain and simple. God gave Adam and Eve ONE rule to follow. That's the rule Satan wanted them to break because he knew what would happen. He didn't try to get them to eat from the "tree of life," it was "the tree of knowledge" he was after. So he conned Eve into breaking that one rule. The fruit of the tree of knowledge of good and evil. It was forbidden by God. Why didn't the Creator want us to have that knowledge? Because it was of the devil? Because with it Satan could deceive us further?

As it is, knowledge turned out to be what we craved. We feasted on that forbidden fruit daily. We continue to gorge ourselves and we call it wisdom.

So...now what would you say drives a person to seek a higher education? To gain as much forbidden fruit as they can to be successful in their chosen profession? And when they think they know all there is to know, the world and technology introduce a bunch of new stuff. There's never an end to it.

Kiz realized that the hunger for knowledge and education stemmed from that first sin. Was that part of the death? One of the consequences of Eve's actions? An all-consuming desire to know more so there would be more to covet? An ever increasing demand from the world for more?

That hunger will never be filled. It will remain and grow ever more ravaging because it is sin that is driving it. Satan and his world are frantically pushing us to be things God never intended us to be.

The grading system only reinforced Kizzy's belief that education was evil. You must retain this amount of worldly knowledge or there's something wrong with you. You are stupid. You'll never amount to anything. You MUST learn more deeply about the things of the world and all of the intricacies it requires.

You must go deeper into places and things you should be leaning away from. If you don't learn what the world wants you to learn you will be a failure. A big fat F. You are no good. You are looked down upon and harassed by the establishment. You won't get any references because you are lacking and lazy. You are stupid and not up to par. If you can't or won't perform to the world's standards you will probably be put on drugs to force you to conform.

But...if your grades are good, you are conforming nicely. You are counted among the best and brightest. You are rewarded richly for your efforts. The accolades are never ending. Everything the world has to offer is easily within your grasp. People present awards to you. The best, highest paying jobs are yours. Expensive homes, clothing and accessories, flashy cars. Food fit for kings. You can have it all. You have become adept at the ways of the world, they have become habit, you don't give them a second thought. You are a good student. Good, good student. Come on, the world is waiting to devour you.

Yes. It had all fallen into place for Kizzy. The higher your education the more of a prisoner you had become. More of a slave to money and the evil one.

"O that there were such an heart in them, that they would
fear Me, and keep all My Commandments always,"
In Deuteronomy 5:29

No one feared God. The only fear Kiz could see in people was fear of reprisal for failing to keep up with the world.

"Take heed therefore how ye hear,"
In Luke 8:18

How were Christians hearing? What were they thinking? Were they thinking? What were they listening to? Kizzy wondered why we had very little interest in God's Words, but were gobbling up the words of the world. Why were we spending so MUCH time listening to the world and so LITTLE time listening to God? Did anyone bother to digest what was in the Bible? Or were we gluttonously too full of other things?

"ever learning, and never able to come to the
knowledge of the truth."
2 Timothy 3:7

Kiz remembered being very excited, tingly as a matter of fact. She somehow associated that tingly, crawling skin experience with the movement of the Spirit. She couldn't recall if it was the second or third Church she had attended. She guessed that part didn't matter. She was on her way to her first Wednesday night Bible study ever.

Oh, how she looked forward to reading and discussing the Word with other believers. She had a voracious appetite for the Bible and waited in delight to see what the Word would reveal and how it would change her life.

When one of the women announced that a quiet voice had spoken to her as she was entering the Church a few months ago, Kiz listened with anticipation. The woman confided that the voice instructed her to go back to school.

Kiz had cringed. The deceiving small, still voice. We automatically assumed it was a Word from God, but we don't bother to check with the Handbook to make sure it's in line with what the Lord commands us to do.

The woman confessed she had put her family in extreme financial hardship to do it. It wasn't even something she was interested in and wasn't sure she would be able to get a job in that field when she was done. It ate up all of her free time.

Her talk of school and her experiences ate up all of the Bible study time. Week after week she replayed what happened at school. She gossiped about classmates, putting them down and making herself out to be the choicest of students.

The Bible study leader tried again and again to return the conversation back to the study, but the woman would only get louder and continue her account of her education. She made sure the spotlight was always on her.

Attendance started to drop. Kiz finally quit going and heard later it had been cancelled altogether. She could easily see Satan's distracting hand in the situation.

Any higher or continuing education was out of the question for her. The only knowledge or wisdom she deemed of any value was what the Spirit would give her.

> *"all Scripture is given by inspiration of God, and is*
> *profitable for doctrine, for reproof, for correction, for*
> *instruction in righteousness: That the man of God may*
> *be perfect, thoroughly furnished unto all good works."*
> *2 Timothy 3:16,17*

This seemed to be the only education suitable for anyone concerned with their spiritual lifetime. From what Kizzy thought she knew of the Bible, it seemed to call us to a much simpler, unencumbered life. Trying to find the narrow gate.

Chapter 8

"But he that knew not, and did commit things worthy of
stripes, shall be beaten with few stripes."

Is it better not to read the Bible? This makes it sound like it might be. Ignorance of the Law. But the Law is still broken. We are still sinning. Wasn't ignorance kind of related to ignore? Disregard or pay no attention? Kiz was sure it was. Ignore something important so you could be ignorant of it? So all these years she had been ignoring God's Word. She wasn't ignorant of it at all. Well, parts of it maybe. How many other Christians were doing the same thing? Ignoring God's Law? Ignoring what Jesus had done for our sorry hides. Why were we doing this?

It finally dawned on her that she was living under Someone Else's Authority. What she called hers was really not. It was being loaned or given to her only for the time she was here. She was more than welcome to use whatever she needed. But how much did she really need? It all still belonged to the One who had made it and owned it.

It was too late for her to stop reading the Bible, too late to claim she didn't know. The fact that she did know chilled her to the bone. Was deliberate ignoring forgiven? She wondered how it could be. If you truly loved the Lord how could you disregard the Laws you were supposed to be living by? She knew she deserved a good many stripes.

"Man shall not live by bread alone, but by every
Word that proceedeth out of the Mouth of God."
In Matthew 4:4

"And that servant, which knew the Lord's Will, and
prepared himself not, neither did according to His Will,
shall be beaten with many stripes,"
Luke 12:47

"Ye do err, not knowing the Scriptures…"
In Matthew 22:29

Kiz may have erred in trying to put the puzzle together. Some things were taken out of context, but was the important thing being she was trying? At this rate she was going to be at it for the rest of her life. She smiled. It was alright with her.

Isn't this what a Christian should be doing? Because of it, she had been finding out that the path she had been traveling was pretty darn wide. There were a great many cracks that needed to be repaired, many things she had been praying wrongly for.

Maybe putting the pieces together in this manner wasn't for everyone. She was sure theologians would be happy to tear her methods apart and explain all of the mistakes she was making, but it worked for her. The pieces no matter how abstract they looked to anyone else, made sense to her. Plus, she was absolutely sure the Spirit was leading her. Her eyes were on the Word of God. It was important to her that it be that way.

Unrepentant sin showed itself to her in the form of pouring herbicide on a vegetable garden because she was too lazy mentally to pull out the weeds or work the ground. Alas, because of repeated use, no more weeds grew there, but nothing important did either. There was no fruit (or vegetables) to show for her labor (or lack of it).

Just dead, barren ground. Mental work, Scriptural work was becoming a necessity. She decided she better get on the ball and start obeying the Rules if she planned to live under Divine Authority.

"Search the Scriptures"
In John 5:39

One of the comments Christians made to her was about the Old Testament. Some say we are living under a New Covenant and the Old Testament is moot nonsense. None of it applies to us anymore. Then why did Jesus say to search the Scriptures? The Old Testament was all that existed in Jesus' time. There was no New Testament yet.

"one jot or one tittle shall in no wise pass from the Law."
in Matthew 5:18

If it was not to be looked at or learned from, why would Jesus say this? Kiz believed everything in it mattered a great deal or God wouldn't have included any of it. So study it she did. It eventually showed her one thing she was praying wrongly for was peace on earth. It may have been peaceful at one time, but since Eve disobeyed, peace left the scene.

She was a little embarrassed to realize that particular prayer showed a complete lack of knowledge about the Bible. It was contrary to God's Will and Kiz wondered if it would hinder the coming of Christ Jesus in some way.

She wondered how long sin, disobedience and disbelief would affect the earth. As long as Jesus stayed away was the answer she got. Did that mean HER sin, disobedience and disbelief could have effects lasting that long? Probably it could, considering she was an average Christian and her negligence to perform her duties properly may have led to someone else not hearing the Words she should have spoken.

How many times in her past was she supposed to put the Great Commission into action but didn't because she wasn't solidly committed to what she claimed to believe? She was thankful for the 60 plus years she had been given, instead of just 16 or so. My how she had changed.

And her prayers had changed, too. Instead of praying for Jesus to come back soon, she looked at young people who were living in sin and prayed for their eyes, ears, minds and hearts to be opened to the truth. If SHE had been changed, THEY could be changed, too.

"and God saw that it was good."
In Genesis 1:12

Kizzy could never know what God considered "good." She imagined it to be pristine, as pure as pure could be. Perfect. Perfect as mere humans could never know. That is how she started to picture peace. Was it all in the mind? That would never happen because the world, Satan's domain, would never allow it. If peace was lovingly putting up with anything and everything everybody wanted to do, God would not allow it. Not for long anyhow. Peace was different in everyone's eyes.

So why waste your time praying for it? It was a noble gesture, but useless. Were we wishing and hoping for a utopia? Perfection that could never exist anywhere on this plane? It may have existed at one time, but not anymore. Satan, sin and disobedience had seen to that.

"Suppose ye that I have come to give peace on earth?
Nay; but rather division:"
Luke 12:51

There wouldn't be peace on earth because God's Word declared it.

"and let us put on the armour of Light."
In Romans 13:12

Why would we need armour if there was going to be peace?

"From going to and fro in the earth, and from
walking up and down in it."
In Job 1:7

How can there be peace when Satan is still wreaking havoc?

"Ye stiffnecked and uncircumcised in heart and ears, ye
do always resist the Holy Ghost: as your fathers did, so do ye."
Acts 7:51

Would there ever be peace as long as people disobeyed and went their own way? Not hardly and that wasn't going to change any time soon. Kiz decided it wasn't profitable to pray for peace on this planet. It wasn't going to happen until Jesus said it was going to happen. And praying for Him to come soon could possibly damn someone who was unsaved to hell for all eternity. That was pure selfishness.

"Blessed are they which are persecuted for righteousness' sake: for theirs is the Kingdom of Heaven. Blessed are ye, when men shall revile you, and persecute you, and shall say all manner of evil against you falsely, for My sake."
Matthew 5:10,11

"if they persecuted Me, they will also persecute you."
In John 15:20

"But he that shall endure unto the end, the same shall be saved."
Matthew 24:13

"If we suffer, we shall also reign with Him:"
In 2 Timothy 2:12

"being reviled, we bless; being persecuted, we suffer it:"
In 1 Corinthians 4:12

Kizzy came to find out through her enlightenment that there would never be peace because of a sequence of events that took place a very long time ago. There is good reason Christians are persecuted and Kiz made it onto many a person's black list because of her views. She did not pray for an end to persecution, there wasn't going to be an end until Jesus returned.

She did not pray for safety and protection of brothers and sisters in countries where they were persecuted the hardest. What she prayed for them was the strength and courage not to deny Christ, no matter what happened to them.

Jesus said it was going to happen until the end. The last war was going to be a battle between the forces of Good and evil. A religious war. And it had been in the beginning stages before Christ was killed. It was getting worse every day. It was not going to get better. Just ask ISIS.

Religious wars were taking place in this country already. Besides that, she could see it happening in milder forms all around her.

As legislation was putting one restriction, muffling or standard in place there were dozens more waiting in line behind it. Yes, progressive and liberal were bringing the end times closer. Sometimes it felt like things were fast forwarding out of control.

Kiz personally felt it would be much better for her to be killed proclaiming her love for the Light of the world than it would be to die a long, lonely, painful death of old age. Everyone she knew strongly disagreed with her. Yep, that Kizzy was a true nutcase. She even wondered sometimes herself if she was crazy.

> *"Get thee behind Me, Satan: for thou savourest not the*
> *things that be of God, but the things that be of men."*
> *In Mark 8:33*

Kiz contemplated this for a very long time. Jesus was sent for the very purpose of suffering and death. It was God's Will. So why did we dare to think that we or anyone else was exempt? Why did we think it was our job to alleviate suffering? Because we savored the things of men and not of God?

She wondered how many times Jesus had thought this same thing about her. Plenty, she was sure. How could she know the Will of God if she didn't know the Word of God?

> *"And behold, the Word of the Lord came unto him, saying,*
> *This shall not be thine heir; but he that shall come forth out of*
> *thine own bowels shall be thine heir."*
> *Genesis 15:4*

Kiz knew that Abram was old at this time and had no children. His wife Sarai was also old.

> *"In the same day the Lord made a covenant with Abram,*
> *saying, Unto thy seed have I given this land, from the river of*
> *Egypt unto the great river, the river Euphrates."*
> *Genesis 15:18*

Abram was to have many descendants and this was to be their land, but because of unbelief and making things happen their own way, only part of them would be entitled. The son of the Promise, not the son of the flesh would inherit the land.

> *"Now Sarai Abram's wife bare him no children, and she had*
> *an handmaid, an Egyptian, whose name was Hagar. And*
> *Sarai said unto Abram, Behold, now, The Lord hath*
> *restrained me from bearing: I pray thee, go in unto my maid;*
> *it may be that I may obtain children by her. And Abram*
> *harkened unto the voice of Sarai. And Sarai Abram's*
> *wife took Hagar her maid the Egyptian, after Abram had*
> *dwelt ten years in the land of Canaan, and gave her to*
> *her husband Abram to be his wife. And he went in unto*
> *Hagar, and she conceived..."*
> *Genesis 16:1-4a*

The nationality, Egyptian, stuck out to Kizzy and she thought about what she could remember about Egypt. Pharaoh did not fear God and said he didn't know this God that Moses and Aaron were talking about. She knew that Egypt was now mostly a Muslim country. Had it always been? When did that start? She had no idea.

She remembered reading a Church sign that said: "Muslims, Jews and Christians all worship the same God." Was Abram's first son raised as a Muslim? Kiz was sure she heard or read that Abram and Sarai taught Hagar about the One True God and that the angel of God spoke to Hagar. But could she still be Muslim? Kiz had no way of knowing.

"And the angel of the Lord said unto her, Behold, thou art with child, and shalt bear a son, and shalt call his name Ishmael: because the Lord hath heard thy affliction. And he will be a wild man; his hand shall be against every man, and every man's hand against him; and he shall dwell in the presence of all his brethren."
Genesis: 16:11,12

Kiz wondered what Hagar thought when she heard that her son would be a fighting troublemaker. Well, that's what it sounded like to Kizzy anyway. What could she do? She would have a son and his destiny was set.

"and God said, Sarah thy wife shall bear thee a son indeed; and thou shalt call his name Isaac: and I will establish My covenant with him for an everlasting covenant, and with his seed after him. And as for Ishmael, I have heard thee: Behold, I have blessed him and will make him fruit- ful, and will multiply him exceedingly; twelve princes shall he beget, and I will make him a great nation. But My covenant will I establish with Isaac, which Sarah shall bear unto thee at this set time in the next year."
Genesis 17:19-21

Kiz was aware of at least one other time in the Bible where the first son was cheated out of his birthright. Could this mean trouble?

"For Sarah conceived, and bare Abraham a son in his old age, at the set time of which God had spoken to him. And Abraham called the name of his son that was born unto him, whom Sarah bare to him, Isaac."
Genesis 21:2,3

"And Sarah saw the son of Hagar the Egyptian, which she had born unto Abraham, mocking. Wherefore she said unto Abraham, Cast out this bondwoman and her son: for the son of this bondwoman shall not be heir with my son, even with Isaac."
Genesis 21:9,10

S.S. Riley

"in all that Sarah hath said unto thee, hearken unto her voice;
for in Isaac shall thy seed be called. And also of the
son of the bond woman will I make a nation,
because he is thy seed."
Genesis 21:12b,13

"And Abraham rose up early in the morning, and took bread,
and a bottle of water, and gave unto Hagar, putting it
on her shoulder, and the child, and sent her away: and
she departed, and wandered in the wilderness of Beersheba."
Genesis 21:14

Hmm. Kiz thought this over. Normally back in that time the eldest son received the greater share of his father's substance. Here, he got nothing but some bread and water. He was sent away, basically disowned.

Hagar, through no fault of her own was given as a wife, bore the son she was supposed to bear and then was sent away empty-handed. Kiz tried to imagine how Hagar and Ishmael must have felt. Wandering in the wilderness alone. Homeless, afraid, empty, angry.

As Kiz thought, she couldn't see how any of this was going to go well for the descendants of either son. It put her in mind of maybe the Hatfields and McCoys. An all out constant feud. Only this wasn't neighbors, it was family. That made it personal.

"Abraham begat Isaac; and Isaac begat Jacob; and Jacob begat
Judas and his brethren: And Judas begat Phares and Zara of
Thamar: And Phares begat Esrom; and Esrom begat Aram;

And Aram begat Aminadab; and Aminidab begat Naasson;
and Naasson begat Salmon; And Salmon begat Booz of Rachab;
and Booz begat Obed of Ruth; and Obed begat Jesse;
and Jesse begat David the king; and David the king
begat Solomon of her that had been the wife of Urias;

And Solomon begat Roboam; and Roboam begat Abia; and

Abia begat Asa; and Asa begat Josaphat; and
Josaphat begat Joram; and Joram begat Ozias;
and Ozias begat Joatham; and Joatham begat Achaz;
and Achaz begat Ezekias; and Ezekias begat Manasses; and
Manasses begat Amon; and Amon begat Josias;

And Josias begat Jechonias and his brethren, about the time
they were carried away to Babylon: And after they were brought
to Babylon, Jechonias begat Salathiel, and Salathiel
begat Zorobabel;

'And Zorobabel begat Abiud; and Abiud begat Eliakim; and
Eliakim begat Azor; and Azor begat Sadoc; and Sadoc begat
Achim; and Achim begat Eliud; and Eluid begat
Eleazor; and Eleazor begat Matthan; and Matthan
begat Jacob; And Jacob begat Joseph the husband of Mary,
of whom was born Jesus, who is called Christ."
Matthew 1:2-16

Kiz could see how what she had heard was true. The firstborn was completely denied and the Messiah came from the lineage of the second born son. People didn't keep their mouths shut about what they perceived to be wrongs and abuses, even if it was the Will of God.

As many generations as there were between Isaac and Jesus, there were between Ishmael and his descendants. It explained why Muslim extremists were persecuting Christians with a vengeance. There would not be peace on earth as long as Muslim extremists and Christians lived on the same planet.

Their religious beliefs were completely opposite. We may worship the same God, but that is as far as it goes. An end to trouble wasn't going to come anytime soon. It was only going to escalate.

Kiz pondered what the world would be like if Sarai and Abram hadn't taken matters into their own hands, if they had believed God and had not gone their own way in producing the promised son.

S.S. Riley

"But as then he that was born after the flesh persecuted him that was born after the Spirit, even so it is now."
Galatians 4:29

Chapter 9

"but many shall cleave to them with flatteries."
In Daniel 11:34

"The Lord shall cut off all flattering lips."
In Psalm 12:3

"a flattering mouth worketh ruin."
In Proverbs 26:28

"For I know not to give flattering titles; in so doing my
Maker would soon take me away."
Job 32:22

Kiz strongly desired to be in the Church. With other believers, worshipping the Creator, giving thanks for all there was. Most especially for the Holy Son of God. Some time after leaving the first Church, she decided to try another one that was not affiliated with it. Maybe things would be different. She prayed things would be different. The next one was, but not in what she believed was a good way.

The building was old and decaying. There was plastic stapled over the stained glass windows. It billowed, puffing and deflating with the breezes. And it was dirty. These things didn't bother her so much as it felt cold. Not heat cold, just cold.

She was excited to be back in a place of worship. She had missed it terribly. With a huge smile on her face, she made her way to the sanctuary. Not a whole lot of people, but enough. Kiz looked at each face expectantly as she passed. No response from anyone. No one even so much as looked at her. They passed in silence, looking at the floor. There were small groups of people laughing and talking all around her so it wasn't a worship kind of silence.

Where's the love? She wondered. She felt love in her heart for these people, her brothers and sisters. No greeting of any sort from anyone except one usher. He gave her a bulletin, showed her to a seat, then sat down in front of her.

Finally some music started and a gentleman got on the stage. He made a long, flowery introduction and a woman ran up the steps holding a microphone. The music got louder. She sang a solo. Then another one. And another one.

Everyone stood and gave her a standing ovation. It lasted a good two minutes. Was someone shouting praises to the "first lady" of the Church? Apparently they were because when the clapping and whooping died down, the man came back onstage, thanked the first lady then asked for another round of applause. The congregation was more than happy to oblige. There was whistling this time. Kiz felt a creepy feeling.

Some announcements were made and a screen was lowered. Words to a song appeared. Finally some participation Kiz thought. The first lady came back with a few other people and everyone sang. Then the sermon, which was fine. The preacher did some praying, the offering was taken and the first lady sang another solo. Another standing ovation and the service was over.

No one looked at Kiz or spoke to her on her way out.

She went back the next week. Same treatment. Was she invisible? She got a bulletin and found a seat. The usher came and sat in front of her again. She noticed that the first lady was sitting in the front row with the preacher. Must be his wife.

The same gentleman came onstage. Same long, flowery intro and the first lady ran on stage. Kiz noticed the preacher seemed to be exploring his face with his tongue as he watched his wife perform.

It was like watching a train wreck or driving past a car wreck. She didn't want to look, but couldn't take her eyes away. Was he really trying to get his tongue into his ear? Kizzy shivered.

Kiz went back the next four Sundays. Maybe someone would start to warm up to her. She hadn't been much of a Church goer for most of her life, but she had read and studied the Word extensively. Even though she had done it in a blinded state, she still understood some of it. What she had encountered in the last Church and this one was not what the Bible had prepared her for. Somehow she expected something much… well, much deeper, more loving, more Christ centered.

This was like a first lady fan club. A club she couldn't see herself being a member of. She was a fan of Christ and she hoped to be around people who felt the same way. Kiz didn't want to come to Church to watch a show. Somehow it felt improper. She didn't care to watch a woman sing and dance for over half the service. She decided the standing ovations, whooping, hollering and whistling over a person was too worldly for her.

On her last visit there were so many distractions from what she had come for, she decided she would not be returning. Too many things were filling her mind and none of them concerned God OR Jesus. She could not worship here.

Her walk with Jesus had become too important to her. What He had done was too amazing to be buried under all of this show. This Church was a path she didn't want to be on anymore. It felt like a wide path that wasn't taking her where she needed to go.

Kiz knew it would be rude to walk out in the middle of the performance so she gazed around. Her eyes, of course, came to a stop on the preacher. He was particularly avid in the exploration of his face today. She couldn't stop watching.

Kiz finally forced herself to look at the stage. Strange, no one had bothered to look at her or speak to her in the six weeks she had been coming, but now she seemed to be facing an angry mob. A LOT of people were looking at her. Not one face looked friendly. She smiled and nodded her head in greeting. She imagined they thought she was lusting after the man. Let them think it, it wasn't true. They could worship the first lady if they wanted to, but she had other plans.

Kiz gathered her things slowly and quietly. She couldn't even begin to fathom the grief she was feeling.

Chapter 10

"And God said, Behold, I have given you every herb bearing
seed, which is upon the face of all the earth, and
every tree in the which is the fruit of a tree yielding seed;
To you it shall be for meat."
Genesis 1:29

"every herb bearing seed…the fruit of a tree yielding seed."
In Genesis 1:29

Hey, Paul, what's up?

Not much. Have a seat. Just cleaning out some old files. What brings you around?

This. I brought you something.

A pear? Gee thanks.

Not just any pear, Paul. It has a problem

A pear with a problem. Is it serious?

I believe so.

It looks fine to me. Are you sure it has a problem?

Well maybe not this one, but others have had problems.

How did you discover this problem?

Well Paul, I have a very unusual neighbor. He's six and every time he sees me he asks if I have anything for him.

That explains it.

No, I'm getting to the point here. Please be patient.

OK.

He asks for stuff like snails or frogs or turtles. But his favorite thing is tree seeds. Do you know any six-year olds that want tree seeds?

Can't say that I do.

Well, I bought a plastic box that's divided into eighteen little compartments on the inside.

I know the kind you're speaking of.

I've been collecting tree seeds for him. A different kind in each compartment with a little slip of paper explaining what kind of seed it is.

And the pear has a problem?

Yes…well I think it does.

I'm listening.

I was at the market getting some fruit and vegetables. Keeping in mind that I still needed tree seeds, I selected three pears.

S.S. Riley

You selected?

I picked up, okay? I picked up three pears. When I got home I peeled off a sticker, washed the pear, got out the cutting board and knife. I was prepared to eat a pear and add pear seeds to the tree seed box. When I cut it in half I was disappointed. No, disappointed is the wrong word. Shocked is more like it.

Shocked? At a pear?

There were no seeds. Nothing. The pear itself was firm but the center where the seeds should have been was a slushy mess. Not even the beginning stages of anything that could reproduce. Here, let me show you.

On my desk?

It will clean up easily enough. Look.

I see what you mean. Yes I'd say this pear has a problem.

See how the stem grows down toward the center and then....

Nothing. Mush. No crisp, fibrous dividing walls, no pips. Did you eat it?

No, I didn't eat it. How could I?

What are you thinking?

I don't know that it's true, but I've heard stories that when the government subsidizes farms they tell you what you have to grow. It seems I remember hearing that whole, perfectly healthy orchards have been destroyed and stuff like this planted in it's place.

Trees that can't reproduce?

How do they get pollinated?

I have no idea.

Remember when you did the research on the sterility that vaccinations cause?

Yes. I was flabbergasted that it was true.

Reproduction has to take place through complicated medical procedures. Expensive ones. I believe the government is gaining control over what can reproduce and how it's done. Take seedless grapes for example. Much more convenient to eat, but we can't grow our own grapes unless we buy the plants.

Or children. Or pears.

When is the last time you ate an orange with seeds in it?

Can't say that I remember.

I looked in several stores and all I could find were naval oranges.

No seeds.

No seeds. Where do the trees come from if there aren't any seeds?

Good question. Labs I suppose. I have no idea.

I smell Satan's influence at work in this. He'll make sure nothing is left pure and unadulterated. Everything the Good Lord made for us is being systematically taken away. Right out from under our noses. It's all being genetically altered. Including us. What can we do about it?

Nothing I suppose. Now that you mention it. No one cares about this you know. As long as there's food on their table, what does it matter? They don't seem to notice. They don't understand how Satan is at work.

Brainwashed. Thinking all is well with the world when it really isn't.

There's no way out of this mess.

Are you forgetting about Jesus? He gave us a way out.

Oh. I'm not forgetting about Jesus. He's the only One that keeps me sane and gives me any kind of hope at all.

So you're sane?

Not by normal standards, no.

Me either. So you want me to dig around and see what I can come up with about non-reproducing plants?

If you want, I'd appreciate it. You don't have to.

But I will. I'd like to know myself. Something else along those lines has been bothering me anyhow.

What's that.

Well, last spring I went to buy a few plants for the garden. They all looked okay, don't get me wrong, but not much was edible when it matured. The broccoli was sour, the cauliflower never went into heads. I had never heard of any of the tomato varieties but I bought two kinds anyway. One got huge green fruit on it and I was pretty excited but they cracked and rotted before they ripened. The other kind got small orange fruit. They were the most disgusting, bitter things I ever ate. The whole mess went right into the trash.

You didn't compost it?

No. Something just felt wrong.

Will you try again?

Oh yes, but I ordered a couple of heirloom seed catalogs. I'll try that. It's got to be better than what I've been getting. Besides, God's originals can't be beat.

But man is trying to outdo Him, huh.

Yeah. With Satan's guidance.

Do you think stuff like those pears is any good for us? Could they be harming people?

Another good question. I'll see what I can find out. What's your long term theory on this whole deal?

Besides everything being ruined on a permanent level, I'd say compliance.

Compliance?

Yes. Force people to conform. If you can't, won't or don't live up to the terms specified in the subsidy agreement, the government comes in and destroys the source of your income. The non-reproducing plants they provided. Then they will probably seize your property because you can't pay the taxes. Plus…

You think there's more?

Of course. Power and control. On top of that, there's a diminished food supply. Evil things are in the works, you mark my words. But I don't think anyone will believe it.

We do.

Yeah, we do, but what can a couple of unimportant schmucks say?

No one will listen. It's all big money.

For the big guy, yes. You think we should try?

There's no point. We're out numbered. And at this point we don't have any solid proof. Just supposition and a whole lot of questions that probably can't be answered truthfully.

And discernment. Listening to the Higher Power.

S.S. Riley

People don't listen. They brush stuff off. There's too much going on to pay any attention to a passing thought.

That isn't a passing thought at all.

No, not at all. Listen, I have to go. You'll keep me updated on what you can find?

Of course. We're in this together buddy. Take care. I'll call you soon.

See you later. Thanks.

No problem.

Chapter 11

*"But I fear, lest by any means, as the serpent beguiled
Eve through his subtlety, so your minds should be
corrupted from the simplicity that is in Christ."*
2 Corinthians 11:3

Hmm…the simplicity that is in Christ. The Narrow Way. Simplicity…simply simple. Plain.

Try as she might, Kiz couldn't recall the sequence of events that brought her to man's meddling in the food supply. She knew that all plants were perfect the way the Lord designed them.

She really didn't pay much attention to what she ate until things started getting complicated for her. Her neck and shoulder on the left side started to hurt. It felt heavy in that area and she had no energy or desire to do anything. She struggled through the days, forcing herself to go to work.

She spent sometimes whole days watching TV. Truthfully unable to get up. Depression set in and she cried a lot. Just being alive was a chore. Everything was neglected including the Lord. She even had no energy to fix food for herself. Anything to put in her stomach was fine.

Idle hands are the devil's playground. Kiz contemplated suicide, she felt so bad. Instead of turning to the Lord as she should have, she struggled on by herself.

One morning she awoke with no strength at all. Her neck and shoulder were burning. She was pretty sure it was her heart. Finally, in desperation, Kiz's knees hit the floor. "Lord, I will not go to the doctor. I don't care if I die. You are the Great Healer and I trust You with my life. If it's my time to go, please give me the strength and courage to do it with grace. If it isn't time for me to pass over, please tell me what I need to do to get better. Thank You."

Kizzy crawled back up onto the bed. Waiting and listening. As she lay there the thought came into her mind of a plant, a tree. She couldn't remember what it was.

She forced herself to her feet and walked to the bookcase. Natural Remedies. There it was. Hawthorn. Now she remembered. It was supposed to be the best thing for the circulatory system.

She poked at her hair with a brush, pulled on some jeans, a baggy sweatshirt over her pajama top and out the door she went. There was a health food store a little over a mile away. It took every bit of strength she could muster to do the job and get home with the tea.

Slowly she sipped down a cup and went to sleep. When she woke up, a voice in her head told her to drink three full glasses of water a day along with five fresh fruits and vegetables. Water? She didn't drink water!

Kiz had been misled by evil before and was never 100% sure of anything she heard in her head. But, if it was from the Lord she needed to obey. She did know that much and this really wouldn't cause any harm if she did it.

> *"prove thy servants, I beseech thee, ten days; and*
> *let them give us pulse (vegetables) to eat, and water to drink."*
> Daniel 1:12

Kiz cried because of tiredness as she searched the kitchen for fruits and vegetables. Her favorite food group had always been sweet stuff. Baked goods. A dried out orange, a rotten apple, moldy carrots and a bag of greenish black mush that had once been celery was all she could find. There were cookies, snack cakes, pudding, etc. of course. Those things had probably helped put her in the condition she was in.

She forced herself once again into the car.

Kizzy really didn't care for very many things in the produce aisle, but she picked a small assortment and ate a banana on the way home. The bags were put on the table. She laid back down, sipping at a glass of water.

She hadn't known how sick she really was until she found it was almost a week before she could down her required quota of stuff. Then she made a chart and crossed off what she had consumed so she wouldn't lose track. She continued to struggle with getting dressed and going to work. It was hard, but it had to be done.

> *"and at the end of ten days their countenance appeared fairer*
> *and fatter in flesh than all the children which did*
> *eat of the king's meat."*
> Daniel 1:15

Kizzy gradually started to feel better. She began noticing how badly things had been neglected while she was out for the count. Then she remembered. Down on her knees she went. Thank You, Lord. She started cleaning up the messes and found that the more she did, the more energy she had.

The depression was gone and the pain in her neck and shoulder was lessening. Kizzy kept up with the five fruits and vegetables, two cups of the tea and three glasses of water until at the end of a few months she actually felt quite well.

Then she slacked off and the symptoms started coming back. She started again but was haphazard about it. Some days she did, some she didn't.

It wasn't until after the meltdown later that she realized if God had told her to do it, she'd best obey. Obedience was all important now and it mattered to her to do it. She made sure she did the routine every day. Always. No matter what.

"And it shall come to pass, that when they make a long blast
with the ram's horns, and when ye hear the sound of
the trumpet, all the people shall shout with a great shout;
and the wall of the city shall fall down flat,"
In Joshua 6:5

Kiz was strongly becoming a believer that the solution to some of her troubles wasn't WHAT the Lord told her to do, it was in the obedience of doing it. Like in the appearance of fleas on her two dogs in late summer. She asked God what to do without using deadly chemicals. She discerned that she was to put baby powder somewhere on the dogs once a day and sweep the carpet twice a day until it got cold.

She didn't see how that was going to accomplish anything but she did it. When the first snow flew, the dogs quit scratching. Kiz swept twice a day for another week just for good measure.

"And the Lord God took the man, and put him into
the garden…"
In Genesis 2:15

As the prayer for whatever little knowledge and wisdom the Lord wanted her to have was being answered, the deeper she thought about what she read in the Bible. Insight was being given to her a little at a time. Reading the Bible before seemed to have been preparation for this. Old passages took on new life and meaning.

God put man in the garden. He knew what was best for us under all circumstances. Because of Satan's influence, we rebelled against God's Wisdom and decided what was best for ourselves. We were put in the garden to tend it, dress it and eat from it. Was there more?

Kiz tried to put to use some of the general knowledge she had learned before she dropped out of school. Man breathes in oxygen and breathes out carbon dioxide. Plants breathe in carbon dioxide and breathe out oxygen. Coincidence? Not in her mind.

S.S. Riley

The healthiest place in the world for a person to be was around plants. The healthiest place for plants to be was around people. The two supported each other on more levels than one. No, of course plants didn't eat people the way man was intended to eat plants, but in return for supplying man with fruit, man took care of the plants.

There was an All Knowing Design in place, a natural connection between man and nature. That's probably why Satan was influencing fear in people. Don't let your kids play outside. Don't get dirty. There are too many germs. You'll get snatched. You'll get run over by a bus. You might be allergic to something. Something might bite you. Stay in the house where it's safe. Keep the windows and doors closed. The air is dirty. Use a machine to circulate and filter that dirty air.

Kiz couldn't even think of all the excuses to stay away from outside. She knew fear was a factor and suspected laziness played a big role, too. Plus, with all of the attention being focused on electronic devices, outside seemed boring. There was nothing to do.

Oops! Her mind was wandering again. She brought it back to her original train of thought.

Bit by bit, pieces of information had been presented to her on genetically modified organisms. After a while she began to wonder if these mutant plants were being altered to upset this fundamental balance between nature and man. Would they still possess the DNA to breathe out oxygen or was that being taken away or damaged?

With Satan's hand in the mix, it wouldn't surprise her at all. If the leaves of a potato plant were so poisonous that they killed anything that grazed on them, what did those potatoes do to people?

When we walked away from raising our own food we started playing Russian roulette with our lives. And with our souls?

"Therefore the fathers shall eat the sons..."
In Ezekiel 5:10

Kiz was sick to her stomach and cried when she heard the news story on the radio. More evil in an already evil world. Researchers in medical science had isolated what they claimed to be a flavor enhancer made from the lining of the cheeks of aborted babies. It was being added to and used by some of the biggest food name brands in the country. And it was true.

We were eating our children and grandchildren and we didn't even know it. As Kizzy pondered the scenario, she was pretty sure those dead babies were soaking in some kind of preservative that had invaded every cell of their tiny, helpless beings. More than likely it was formaldehyde, one of the more potent cancer causing agents known to man.

Not only were we unknowingly being fed aborted fetuses, we were probably being poisoned at the same time. Kiz wondered how many people involved in this abomination claimed to be followers of the Lord.

"fear not…"In many, many verses.

As Kiz wandered the grocery store in a very sad daze, she wondered if anything at all was safe to eat. She watched what fear and advertising was doing to folks. People were using disposable sanitizer cloths to scrub the cart handles, their children's hands and their own, even using them on the children's faces.

They were so worried about a few germs that they were oblivious to the fact it wasn't just germs they were killing. They were using deadly chemicals daily on themselves and their kids. Did they know? Did they care? Had they been brainwashed? Why couldn't they see what they were doing? They were more worried about what was on their shopping carts than they were about what they were putting into them.

There was a little bit of fear eating away at Kiz but there was also a deep sadness that it appeared the evil one had the upper hand. Of course she knew he didn't in the end. But right now it sure looked that way. She tried hard to look forward to that time when Jesus would come in all of His Glory and things would be perfect again.

S.S. Riley

"Better is a dinner of herbs where love is…"
In Proverbs 15:17

No, Kiz couldn't find love anywhere in any of this genetic altering that was going on. To her, it felt more like pure, unadulterated hate. Genetic engineering was being forced on the population without their knowledge or consent by "those in high places." It was sickening livestock, food sources, poultry, plants, everything it touched…including people.

Kizzy knew the evil prince of darkness could not go beyond the boundaries that God set for him. With all of the evil in the world, that told her a lot. She also knew that it wasn't all the devil doing it. We had chosen the wide path instead of the narrow one. A lot of it was our fault.

We were human guinea pigs. Worse, we were victims just like the innocent animals were. Was God allowing us to be punished for our wayward, self fulfilling behavior? From what Kizzy had heard, lab tests involving GMO foods and animals never turned out well. If animals were suffering illness and death, she believed people were, too.

We were demanding so much food and such a big variety of it that we didn't concern ourselves with what it took or where it came from. As long as it was available to us whenever and wherever we wanted it, we were cool.

But all of nature was suffering because of our gluttony. Monarch butterflies were among some of the winged creatures that were being wiped out by poisonous corn pollen. That pollen was driven by the wind to infect non-GMO corn turning it mutant, also. Honey bees collected the pollen and their food supply was tainted. It seemed honey would no longer be a healthy sweetener. Sweet corn was Kiz's all time favorite vegetable; but now it was, by choice, out of her diet.

As Kiz perused the produce, she couldn't tell if any or all of it was genetically altered. So she asked a woman who was putting out lettuce if anything was GMO free. She got a mean stare in return and was told she had no idea.

It didn't have to be necessarily organic. That stuff was priced out of reach. She just wanted to know what hadn't been tampered with. Pesticides and herbicides seemed mild in comparison, but they probably weren't.

Kiz noticed a huge, weird melon and went over to check it out. New! The sign said. Cantaloupe bred to last longer on the shelf! Try one now for this special low price! Special alright. She backed away uneasily and picked out a few things that looked normal. She had been made aware that almost every package of prepared food contained GMO products so she left with very little in her grocery cart.

"In the sweat of thy face shalt thou eat bread..."
In Genesis 3:19

Kiz lived on fruits and vegetables mainly, adding things she prepared herself. It took a while for her garden to get going. She planted grapes with seeds in them, an apple tree, a cherry tree, strawberries, asparagus, onions, garlic and blueberries. She ordered organic seed catalogs and delighted in the vast array of beautiful foods.

She volunteered at a homeless shelter in her city and met a woman who seemed as concerned about the state of the world as she was. Michele suggested that maybe some GMO seeds had gotten into the supply of one of the do-it-yourself programs. Kiz could see how that might happen, so she settled on Baker Creek Heirloom Seeds.

It contained a wealth of knowledge and information. So she sent in an order. Then she decided on a few more things. One of which was a book called "Seeds of Deception," by Jeffrey M. Smith.

As she pondered whether to spend that much more money, her daughter called. She told her about a dream she'd had. Someone died and there was a bag of seeds with $83.00 written on it. You didn't spend $83.00 on seeds did you? No at that point in time she hadn't. Her daughter was relieved at the news.

Kiz sat down and found what she'd already spent, then added to it what she planned to spend. It came to $82.65 with shipping.

Now she played yoyo in her head. Would someone die if she sent the additional order? There was a lot of praying involved. Finally Kiz discerned that she was being preyed upon with fear. Was there information in that book the evil one didn't want her to have? Why? She decided she trusted God no matter what happened. The order was sent and no one died. At least not immediately...

The book was very revealing about a great many things including corruption at all levels of government. Kiz recommended it to anyone who seemed interested.

The garden was a success. She started tomatoes, Brussels sprouts, peppers and kale in the house. Winter in Ohio didn't provide any sunny windows so she set them in south windows. Her son made a cold frame for her and she moved the seedlings into it.

After all was said and done, she had added lettuces, carrots, beets, radishes, green beans, soup beans, peas and marigolds. She did a lot of eating and giving away out of her garden. Some things were dried, canned or frozen.

She wanted to have rabbits, chickens and goats, but she knew any feed she got for them would be GMO and besides, she lived in the city. For now, since she couldn't afford to move, it was impossible.

> *"And that ye may put difference between holy and unholy,*
> *and between unclean and clean;"*
> *Leviticus 10:10*

Kizzy read through the Laws that God gave on food after asking Him for insight. In Leviticus He was giving instruction on the food His people could and could not eat. Why was it clean or unclean? Probably because of it's purpose on the planet and what it ate. But mainly because God SAID it was clean or unclean. He had definite reasons for His Laws.

As for shellfish, is it possible it was an unclean "abomination" because they were bottom feeders? Cleaning up all the filthy debris that made it's way to the sea floor? She remembered that through a dream, God had shown Peter that all things were now clean. Still...Kiz decided that with over a billion people putting all kinds of things down drains into the water supply, she could live without shellfish.

"Let me now go to the field, and glean ears of corn…"
In Ruth 2:2

Kiz also felt the foraging bug eating at her. Things that grew wild and were all around us, free for the taking. They would be nutritious. So far she hadn't tried it except for a few bags of mulberries she had in the freezer. She would use them in her smoothies with other fruits that she liked. Her hope was that she would find someone who was experienced at gathering. She wasn't sure what to pick or what to do with it after she picked it.

"and if they drink any deadly thing, it shall not
hurt them…"
In Mark 16:15-18

Kizzy knew that she could not grow everything she needed. It seemed God had designed humanity to work together. Some things would have to be purchased at the store. So, before ANYTHING went into her mouth, she made sure she had properly thanked the Creators, Father and Son and added a request at the end: "and please, if there is anything evil in what I am about to eat please let it pass through unsuccessfully. Thank You."

She never believed that trying to get away from the polluted and poisoned food supply would do much good or make her anymore healthy. It was impossible to get away from it, it was everywhere.

She wasn't sure why she did it. She didn't think it was to try to reach some kind of unreachable perfection. Could wanting clean, pure food be some sort of idol worship? She tried to examine her motives, but found no solid answers for her rebellion of the wide, wide world's ways. Maybe it was because she loved the Lord deeply and had a great respect for His Creation.

The Lord would have to be her judge on this one. All of glorious creation was being destroyed. One of her favorite things used to be driving in the country looking at beautiful fields of crops. She always thanked God for His bountiful provision. Now she looked at the fields with disgust, knowing it was mostly filthy perversion.

"For we know that the whole creation groaneth and
travaileth in pain…"
In Romans 8:22

Kiz often wondered if plants suffered physical pain with their man- inflicted diseases the same way men suffered physical pain with theirs. Were they also crying out to God for help? She knew the cows, pigs and chickens suffered with pain because of man's meddling. It only stood to reason that plants were suffering also. And all because Eve ate the forbidden fruit.

Chapter 12

"And I will come near to you to judgment; and I will be
a swift witness against the sorcerers...saith the Lord of hosts."
Malachi 3:5

Oh dear. There really was something wrong with her. In Kizzy's old age she had become insane and a stick in the mud. She couldn't describe how she felt when the Church decided to have a down-home Halloween party. It couldn't be shock because it didn't surprise her at all. There was nausea and a numbness in her heart.

It actually hurt her physically to see such a thing. Wasn't the Church supposed to be a place of worship, praise and thanksgiving? How many un-Christian things was this Church being used for? To her it was a disgrace for such a thing to happen.

Everyone was bustling around joyfully. Filling bags with candy, putting up decorations and shaking wrinkles out of costumes from the attics of donors. Parents of children from the neighborhood were asked to bring covered dishes or chips and drinks. Pots of food were bubbling happily on a stove in the dining hall. Preparations were in full swing. This was going to be an all out, no holds barred, A-1, over the top event. The talk of the town for months to come. A celebration to beat all celebrations before it.

Was that a stab of hypocrisy jabbing at her already aching heart? She believed it was. She recalled when her kids were small. She decorated, dressed them up and took them out trick-or-treating. That was before the great awakening. Before her faculties had been opened to recognize the truth. Before, when she had been deceived. Before, when she was blinded to the fact that all of this worldly stuff was along the wide path. Not the narrow one.

Tears came to her eyes as she realized what she had been doing. She knew only the Lord could open her brothers' and sisters' eyes and she prayed for it. She prayed for an awakening in the Church as she had been awakened. But there was a sinking feeling deep within her that, as with an alcoholic, it had to be a personal choice. Not something that was forced on you. That never worked. As long as you didn't see the problem or denied that there even was one, no change would come.

Kiz was out of the loop. She was becoming more and more unpopular. She was the wet blanket over every fun thing anyone did. In truth, she didn't care. Her deepening walk with the Lord had made her want to pull away from what the world considered fun. She still loved the people dearly, but wanted no part in things like this.

It didn't matter that it was for the kids. It didn't matter that the decorations were cutesy. What did matter was the fact that it was a celebration of something rooted in evil. No matter how innocent it looked, it wasn't. What should have been a solemn, holy night preceding All Saints Day had been tramped on and spit at by the world.

As with the after-school program, Kiz stuck by her reasoning. Time, energy, talent, money and resources would be much better spent on something more important. She felt a stronger connection to Jesus as she turned her back and walked away.

The air in the Church behind her was good riddance.

Chapter 13

"And when ye stand praying, forgive…
But if ye do not forgive, neither will your Father
which is in Heaven forgive your trespasses."
In Mark 11:25,26

Jesus made it clear. He said it. And He said we are to live by every Word that proceeded out of the Mouth of God. And He is God.

"So likewise shall My Heavenly Father do also unto you,
if ye from your hearts forgive not every one his
brother their trespasses."
Matthew 18:35

And Jesus also said,

"For if ye forgive men their trespasses, your Heavenly
Father will also forgive you."
Matthew 6:14

And that.

As more understanding of the Word was imparted to her, it made her stop and think. It raised lots and lots of questions in her mind. She prayed a lot, yet she wasn't absolutely sure whether the results she discerned were out of her own mind, the result of evil influence or given to her by the Spirit, the Much Higher Power.

"And when ye stand praying, forgive." She never knew she had to forgive people while she was praying. She thought it was just good enough to do it. But if Jesus said to do it while praying, she best try to remember and oblige. Now she was confronted with the issue of whether or not she had to go all the way back to the beginning and start over. Or could she do it in one big lump up to this point and start from here?

> *"Behold, thou art made whole: sin no more."*
> *In John 5:14*

This had nothing to do with what was on her mind but since it had been drawn to her attention, maybe it was the key. Sin no more. Once you realized your sin against the Word of God, repent. Be sorry you did and correct it.

Her mind went back to the issue of not being forgiven by God. If we didn't forgive, didn't bring all things to the Lord in prayer and supplication, and weren't forgiven, what did God do with us?

> *"He that believeth and is baptized*
> *shall be saved."*
> *In Mark 16;16*

It says we will be saved. But if it isn't forgiven, what will happen? Kiz couldn't recall ever seeing the word "purgatory" in the Bible. It wasn't in the concordance, but a lot of people sure believed in it. Was there something to their belief? Should we just be thankful we were saved and not strive to live by the Word of God?

Kiz vaguely remembered some of what she had read in Dante's "Inferno." It seemed odd to her that whatever lesson he was to be taught was never clearly stated. Maybe just the fact that he never wanted to be in any level of hell. If hell had levels.

She had always wondered what the "being cast into outer darkness" thing was all about. Some told her it just meant hell, but she had some reservations about believing that. Wouldn't it just have said they would be cast into hell? Jesus' Words were not used haphazardly. He meant what He said. Could "outer darkness" possibly be the black holes that scientists were so excited about?

In her mind, Kiz could see evil as a slimy, greenish brown, slow moving glop. It started when Adam and Eve ate the forbidden fruit and infected everything and everyone in it's path.

She had some training in her background as a volunteer for the Rape Crisis Center. She had been told that most lesbians had been raped or molested on a regular basis by some man in their life. They became so repulsed by men that they turned to women for love, support, comfort and companionship.

Likewise with men who had been repeatedly molested by females in their households. They wanted nothing to do with them.

Evil causing more evil.

There was a string of revenge killings going on in and around her neighborhood. She wondered when or if it would ever stop. Forgiveness would stop the ongoing spread of evil, but Satan, egos and tempers would never permit that. It had to stop with sincere believers. We would have to absorb that evil slime and allow it to go no further.

That wasn't going to happen either. Because we hadn't learned or decided to forgive people. Kiz had seen it many times in Churches she had attended. One instance in particular stuck out to her. A woman who was ten years into her second marriage would dominate the table where she sat during fellowship meetings with woes from her first marriage.

She would cry and blow her nose and say how badly her ex-husband had hurt her. Her current husband would turn his back to her, stiffening and crossing his arms across his chest. He would move as far away from her as he could get without leaving his chair.

Everyone else could see it, but the still refusing to forgive woman couldn't. Her seemingly cherished pain was causing distress in others. Her new husband, those at the table who were trapped and uncomfortable. Probably the children of both of them were suffering unnecessarily because of it. Wouldn't it have been so much simpler for all involved if she would just forgive him and let it go?

Jesus didn't give us a suggestion, it was a command. Do it or else. It was even in the prayer the Lord taught His disciples.

Kiz looked back over the miserable life she had made for herself. Being beaten up and abused by drunk boyfriends; waking up in jail; having things stolen; having her heart broken over and over and over again. Almost being killed several times.

Yeah, if she wanted to she could probably come up with a pretty long list of things, wrongs, that had been done to her. But she didn't. She wouldn't. She didn't look at it that way. It would be a selfish waste of time. She let everything go because she wondered how long the list of wrongs she had inflicted on other people would be. She was pretty sure it wouldn't be a very pretty sight.

From time to time events of an ugly nature would enter her mind. She decided that was the time to fall on her knees and tell God she had forgiven. And please forgive her for the sinful part she had played in the creating of the event in the first place. She was not completely innocent in any of it and she knew it. Maybe part of the awfulness had been punishment, maybe part of it had been the pruning process from the Lord.

She felt kind of guilty because she knew un-forgiveness was a lot of heavy baggage to carry around. She wasn't that strong. So she let it all go into the thin air of genuine love and forgiveness. In the holding a grudge department she had become baggage free.

Chapter 14

*"For behold this self same thing, that ye sorrowed after a godly
sort, what carefulness it wrought in you, yea, what
clearing of your selves, yea, what indignation, yea,
what fear, yea, what vehement desire, yea, what zeal,
yea what revenge (vindication!)...
In 2 Corinthians 7:11*

After a short time of not attending any Church and with her tithes safely tucked away in a coffee can, the itch started in her again. Kiz felt a growing desire, no, a growing need to be among believers. It came to almost a bursting point. She knew in her heart that something very important was missing. She had no faith or trust in Churches because of previous experiences and had no idea where to turn.

She made phone calls to several places looking for a diverse congregation and missions to the local community. That's where her heart was. She loved all people and wanted to help where help was needed most. Her calls got her nowhere.

Finally she talked to a friend who suggested a Church in a poor area that had a large number of homeless. It was definitely a diverse area. It sounded perfect to Kiz until she learned it was a sister Church to the first one she had tried. The same conglomeration of bought-out buildings and congregations.

Extreme hesitancy held her back. Then she started reasoning with herself. It was a different pastor, a different area, different people, hopefully a different everything. So she went.

It was small, very small. Maybe twenty-five folks sitting in the pews. All white. Surely not what she had expected, but…She was delighted and her soul tingled as a hymn sing was started. One woman played at a piano and another at an organ. The leader asked who wanted to sing what song. Someone called out a page number and the music started.

A smiling woman handed her a hymnal opened to the right page. Kiz sang her heart out, although not very well. She considered herself to be a pretty lousy singer, but it was the voice the Lord had given her. She hoped at least she was making a joyful noise. After four more old favorites were sung the service started. At least the music in this one set her heart in a serious worship mode.

Kiz listened to every word very carefully. She didn't want to be misled in any way. A few verses were read from the Bible, then the preacher gave what the bulletin called a "reflection." Nowhere did it have the word sermon. She noticed right off that the reflection had nothing to do with the verses that had been read. He read some poetry which meant nothing to her. He talked about things like how he had raked up a bunch of leaves in his yard. There were dead spots where he put down grass seed. And how he noticed something black in the road up ahead and when he got there it was a crow. He seemed to be reflecting about events that had happened to him during the week. She kept her mind open. Maybe it was a one time thing.

> *"Even so faith hath not works, is dead,*
> *being alone."*
> *James 2:17*

Kizzy's heart was seriously drawn to help with the ministries of the Church. There were lunches prepared by other Churches which were brought in and served in the dining hall. Leftover food was packed up and given away. Clothing and household goods that had been donated were spread out on the pews. The community could take what they needed. Feeding and clothing the poor was being fulfilled.

Kiz was making good friends in the Church and in the neighborhood. It energized her to be doing the Lord's work and she thrived on it. She pitched in to help wherever help was needed. From setting up to cleaning up the dining hall, Kiz was in the thick of it. Still, something felt wrong. As in not right. A strange sensation was niggling at her soul.

> *"therefore shall a man leave his father and his mother,*
> *and shall cleave unto his wife: and they shall be one flesh."*
> Genesis 2:24

On entering the Church one Sunday morning, a dear friend approached Kiz. She was crying. If her water bill wasn't paid by tomorrow it would be shut off. She didn't have the money to pay it and was afraid to borrow it because she wasn't sure she would be able to pay it back.

Kiz went looking for the preacher. It had been his habit not to be there quite often and Kiz found out this was the case today. She asked around and found out a woman, a preacher who was part of a lesbian couple was filling in for him.

Kiz was a little shocked. She tried quickly to digest this information and presented the problem at hand to the fill-in preacher. Would it be possible to take up a love offering at the end of the service to help this member of the Church?

Kizzy wanted nothing to be taken away from the regular offering so asked if it could be the final thing. It was okayed. The love offering was taken. The money was given to the woman to pay her water bill. Kiz hoped it would be enough.

Believing things were hunky dory on that part, she turned her prayers and crying to the rampant acceptance of sin in the Church. Was it a pattern in this particular group of Churches to put sexual fornicators and sodomists in positions of power and authority? It looked like it was.

Kiz truly believed that the divorced and gay and lesbian people who decided to live under the Divine Authority of their Lord and King should abide by His Rules and commandments. Wouldn't celibacy be the appropriate path under the circumstances? What did she know? She loved the people, but hated the behavior.

Trying to come to terms with the situation had her preoccupied and she was alarmed by getting an irate phone call from the preacher two days later. How dare she ask for a love offering in HIS church? Things like that didn't happen in HIS Church. There was an institution in place for such things and love offerings were forbidden. Keep in mind that it better never happen again on HIS watch. Goodbye.

Kiz was stunned. It ran against everything in her. Weren't we supposed to help our brothers and sisters in time of need? Wasn't that what we were supposed to do? She noticed there were many things the Church was taking away from God's people. Satan at work for sure.

The next time she saw the fill-in preacher she apologized for getting her into trouble. She had only smiled and said she had broad shoulders. It didn't make Kiz feel any better about any of it.

> *"For the priest's lips should keep knowledge, and*
> *they should seek the Law at his mouth: for he is the messenger*
> *of the Lord of hosts. But ye are departed out of the way;*
> *ye have caused many to stumble…"*
> *In Malachi 2:7,8*

Kiz tried to be pleasant and keep a low profile at the Church after being yelled at. She loved the fellowship and the feeding and clothing of the poverty stricken area. She had made a mistake and gone against the rules of the Church. There were many things she disagreed with, but maybe she was the one who was wrong. She had been wrong many times before.

It was during a community lunch that a young woman approached the preacher. She asked if he would perform a wedding ceremony for her and her boyfriend. He said absolutely not. If she would settle for a covenant ceremony he would be happy to oblige, but until everyone in HIS Church that wanted to be married could be, there would be no weddings. She wanted a legal, binding marriage. He suggested the lesbian preacher who had filled in for him on numerous occasions.

Stunned and shocked couldn't begin to describe how Kiz felt about the exchange she had just heard. She finished out the lunch in a daze.

"But there were false prophets also among the people, even
as there shall be false teachers among you, who privily
shall bring in damnable heresies,"
In 2 Peter 2:1

It was all Kiz could do to keep her chin up. The condition of Churches was way worse than she ever could have imagined. So far removed from Biblical teaching it was scary. But again, what did she know? Who was she to judge? That was God's job. Not hers. Still, she felt as if she were in mourning.

The final time she walked into that church, she found it was All Saints Day. Not having been brought up in a Christian home or Church, she wasn't familiar with all of the Holy Days and seasons. The very name, All Saints Day, felt holy even if it wasn't.

The service began with the beautiful heartfelt hymn sing. Announcements and prayer requests were made. Another song was sung. Several Bible verses about saints were read and then the reflection began.

The preacher read a rather lengthy poem. It sounded to Kiz like all of creation was being worshipped rather than the Creator. Then the preacher went into a solemn story about saints from the Church who had passed since he came there. He named names and acknowledged family members who were still among the congregation. Nothing wrong with that as far as Kiz could see.

Then he walked out of the pulpit, up the aisle and sat down in a pew. This was where so and so sat. We could all rest assured that the electromagnetic soul of so-and-so was still sitting there worshipping with us. Kiz fought desperately to remember anything of the sort in the Bible. It was futile. Her mind was blank.

He got up and moved to another pew. He comforted some family members with the fact that the electromagnetic souls of their loved ones were still sitting there with them. People were weeping quietly and kept saying "amen." After a few more sit-downs with remembrances of dearly departed saints, he returned to the pulpit, smiled and loudly and joyfully reiterated the fact that electromagnetic souls remained among us.

Kiz asked the woman behind her what she thought of the whole deal. It was okay, the important thing is that he is honoring our lost ones. The rest doesn't matter.

Yes! Her mind was screaming. Yes! It does matter. All of it matters. The electromagnetic souls of the dearly departed still sitting in the pews where the dearly sat before they departed? "Lord, help us." Along with everything else that was going on within these walls, Kizzy knew she couldn't come back.

Kiz didn't consider the year and a half as wasted. She had learned a lot and met quite a few wonderful people. Why couldn't she just go with the flow like everyone else seemed to do? Why did she have to complicate everything? Why couldn't she just fit in and accept that things were evil everywhere? She had no answers and no solutions. All she knew about that was, she couldn't accept it and wasn't going to ever fit in.

As Kiz walked out the church doors on that particular all saints day, she silently vowed to herself that she would never set foot in that brand name Church ever again. Never!

She didn't know how wrong she would be. We can never know what God has planned for us.

Chapter 15

"to them that are sanctified by God the Father, and preserved in
Jesus Christ, and called:"
In Jude 1st verse

What an honor. Sanctified by God, preserved in Jesus, called. The thought crossed her mind that being preserved by Jesus was far better than being preserved in formaldehyde or something. Was everyone called or just the chosen? Kiz would have to search for that later. Right now she felt there was something terribly, terribly wrong. Was it with the world? With her? Kiz tried to keep in mind that she could very well be going insane. Why was she feeling this way?

It couldn't be categorized by any of the words she knew, something she couldn't quite grasp. It eluded her, but she believed it involved physical, mental, emotional and spiritual elements all rolled into one big roiling mass. Like maybe there was a volcano getting ready to erupt in her being. She could feel it. Try as she might, pray she did, but still it couldn't be described. All she knew for a fact was that Jesus deserved so much more, so much better than what He was getting.

What she had experienced so far in the Churches she had visited somehow made her angry. Along with the anger she felt pity, distress and sadness. For herself, for all of mankind. Oh how much they had missed, she had missed, under that blinding cloak of deception and distraction.

It lit a fire in her innards that she wasn't sure what to do with. But it burned, as if it was alive.

"So then because thou art lukewarm, and neither hot nor
cold, I will spew thee out of My Mouth."
Revelation 3:16

Everyone, Kiz included, had believed they were right with the Lord. It was easy. Believe and be baptized. Done. Piece of cake. But she had been so very wrong. There was so much more to it.

Kiz tried to discuss the standard tolerance and acceptance of anything and everything that was allowed within the four walls of a Church building. All she could ever get out of anyone was a frozen, condescending smile and tone of voice as if they were trying to get a point across to a stubborn child for the umpteenth time.

"Yes, well, God is the God of love," "The greatest of these is love." "Judge not, lest ye be judged." She knew all of that, but it scared her. They looked like robots, repeating what had been programmed into them. They had a very distorted view of God's Love, what love was in general. She could see the evil one grinning from ear to ear. Make discipline despicable and un-Christian-like and you had just issued a license to everyone to do whatever they wanted, with no penalties due. Until the end, of course.

She could see clearly now that it was all part of Satan's devious plan. And yes, he does have a plan. Make it politically incorrect for believers to even imply there was any kind of penalty for disobedient behavior and Voila!, the stage was set for swift destruction. When you stopped at love, tolerance and acceptance, it meant to her that you hadn't bothered to read any further into the Word. You left out the fine print. You stopped growing spiritually.

Hadn't they read the book of Revelation?

Didn't they know the stories that were meant to instruct us?

"how that the Lord, having saved the people out of the
land of Egypt, afterward destroyed them that
believed not."
In Jude verse 5

"And the angels which kept not their first estate, but
left their own habitation, He hath reserved in everlasting
chains under darkness unto the judgment of
the Great Day."
In Jude verse 6

And we think it won't happen to us?

"Even as Sodom and Gomorra, and the cities about them
in like manner, giving themselves over to fornication, and
going after strange flesh, are set forth an example, suffering
the vengeance of eternal fire,"
In Jude verse 7

Didn't they know that God sent His people into slavery for 400 years?

Or that He made His people to wander in the desert for 40 years until a whole generation died?

Or that Moses was only allowed to see the promised land, but not allowed to go into it because of his impatience and disobedience?

Or that all of mankind was wiped out by a flood except Noah and his family?

"And it repented the Lord that He had made man on the earth,
and it grieved Him at His Heart."
Genesis 6:6

Was God grieved again? Had He always been grieved since the beginning of man?

As Kiz pondered these questions, her heart broke. Oh, how remorseful she was. She had grieved a lot of people in her life, but most importantly she had grieved God. Then she remembered: "Do not grieve the Holy Spirit." Oh man. There was no way she could erase any of the horrid things she had done. But she could be sorry. And she was. She would never do those kinds of things again. Her love for the Lord had grown immensely and this wouldn't be a difficult decision to live with. It was something she dearly wanted to do. Stop being a deliberate sinner.

> *"Was not Esau Jacob's brother? Saith the Lord: yet I loved*
> *Jacob, And I hated Esau."*
> *In Malachi 1:2,3*

It seemed to Kiz that this wasn't the only "I hate" instance she could recall in her Bible. How could the God of love hate? But He did.

Did God expect us to stand up for our belief in His Son? The Christ Child? Kiz thought maybe He did.

Did God hate that evil was rampant in the Churches?

Did God hate that His Son was being disrespected and disregarded?

Did God hate that His Laws, commands and Words were being ignored?

Kiz thought maybe He did. Kiz hated it herself. But again, who was she? What did she know? She was just a wretched sinner.

> *"Blessed are ye, when men shall hate you, and when*
> *they shall separate you from their company, and*
> *shall reproach you, and cast out your name as evil, for*
> *The Son of man's sake."*
> *Luke 6:22*

Kiz was going to stand up for her Savior. She decided she would rather be blessed for being hated than she would have Jesus spew her out of His Mouth for being lukewarm. It appeared to Kiz that what they had allowed into the Churches was a symptom, an overflow of what they had allowed into their lives. Her life. But no more. Everything was going to be scrutinized from here on.

S.S. Riley

> *"But what things were gain to me, those I counted loss*
> *for Christ, Yea doubtless, and I count all things but*
> *loss for the Excellency of the knowledge of Christ Jesus*
> *My Lord: for Whom I have suffered the loss of all*
> *things, and do count them as dung, that I may win Christ."*
> *Philippians 3:7,8*

Kiz didn't watch TV at home anymore, but other people had it on when she visited them in their homes. She recalled that her son was watching a show about the removal of King Tut's mummified remains from his tomb to be examined by the latest scientific technology.

Only Egyptians were allowed access for the procedure. One man quietly and respectfully exclaimed that they were in the presence of a king. They all moved slowly with a solemn demeanor. They were very careful, showing dignity and respect in every movement.

Kiz didn't catch the whole show, but what she saw struck her in a weird way. It showed a deep contrast in cultures. When she had gone to worship services, the person in charge had to call order two or three times before most of the people entered the sanctuary. They continued to talk and laugh until the music threatened to drown them out. Sometimes a ten-o'clock service had to start ten or fifteen minutes late because folks wouldn't settle down.

> *"for He is Lord of lords; and King of kings."*
> *In Revelation 17:14*

There was no dignity or respect shown in any way that Kiz could see. Just everybody talking, wanting someone to hear them. After seeing what she saw, she always entered the sanctuary quietly, avoiding the noisy crowd, preparing herself to participate in worship. Praying, looking through the hymnal, meditating on a stained glass window or a flickering candle. Thinking about her Lord. The Light of the world. Precious Jesus.

When conversations about illnesses, upcoming surgeries or gossip took precedence over worship and praise, Kiz wondered if the invocation for the Lord to be present really worked. Was He there? What did He see? What did He think of what was going on? We were supposed to be in the presence of THE Lord of lords, THE King of kings who above all else demanded loyalty, belief and worship.

The Egyptians showed more devotion to a corpse than we did to the Living God.

> *"on the Seventh Day shall be a solemn assembly to*
> *The Lord thy God:"*
> *In Deuteronomy 16:8*

Since Jesus kept the Sabbath and said the Law was still in effect, shouldn't we be having solemn assemblies?

> *"it is iniquity, even the solemn meeting"*
> *In Isaiah 1:13*

Is that what they were? Iniquity? Kiz did a lot of praying and asking forgiveness. "God, please teach me how to be solemn at Your Feet."

> *"That they all may be one; as Thou, Father, art in Me, and I in*
> *Thee, that they also may be one in us: that the world may believe*
> *that Thou hast sent Me."*
> *John 12:21*

> *"And the Glory which Thou gavest Me I have given them;*
> *that they may be one, even as We are One:"*
> *John 17:22*

> *"For we being many are one bread, and*
> *one body:"*
> *In Corinthians 10:77*

There didn't seem to be any oneness in the Lord. In fact, listening to people talk in Church, their hearts weren't in it. It felt more like a house divided. Or a house distracted? Was it the fault of people like her? Possibly demanding too much from souls who couldn't live up to her expectations? What about the expectations of our Lord Jesus Christ?

She didn't want fluffy, feel-good sermons every week. Once in awhile was okay, but not all the time. Kiz wanted to be convicted, wanted to know what she was doing wrong in her life. She was far from perfect and knew it. She needed to be made aware of when Godly change was needed so she could at least try to work on it.

If a sermon even got close to doing that, people became indignant. Things got ugly. "Who is HE to say things like THAT to ME?" It seemed people didn't want any change in their lives. "HE should get that beam out of his own eye before he starts picking at the speck in MINE!"

Kiz suspected that probably some preachers had tried the truth early in their careers, but didn't have time to address all of the complaints they got. They possibly feared for their lives because of angry mobs.

She sadly resigned herself to the fact that it was going to be flowery, poetic, fluffy, feel good about yourselves sermons for all eternity. After over 2000 years we still hadn't even come close to getting anything right. We seemed to be drifting farther and farther away.

We were all over the map, not even near to the Narrow Path. Kiz had to keep reminding herself that we were only human and there was a really big idol we worshipped. Self. You couldn't worship God and self. It didn't work that way.

"Beware ye the leaven of the Pharisees,"
In Luke 12:1

"Then understood they how that He bade them not beware of
the leaven of bread, but of the doctrine of the
Pharisees and of the Sadducees."
Matthew 16:12

"Know ye not that a little leaven leaveneth
the whole lump?"
In 1 Corinthians 5:6

Kiz was beginning to see why Satan would manipulate bad seed into the Churches. She knew from experience that being around a certain bad behavior for a time would make you start acting that way. People who didn't cuss would pick it up quickly, etc.

It was easy to believe that uncouth people who were around good people would soon start acting good, but it always had the opposite effect. Bad behavior was more easily adapted because it took less thought and effort.

Good behavior required strength, stamina, determination and discipline. It didn't come easily. It was always easier to do the wrong thing than the right thing. Evil leavening spread quickly.

> *"Purge out therefore the old leaven, that ye may*
> *be a new lump,"*
> *In 1 Corinthians 5:7*

Kizzy could see hope. There were a lot of different leavenings within her. The first step was wanting them gone. The second step was figuring out what they were. Then, as the Bible said, purging them. She thought being around other believers would help with this process, but she was sadly mistaken.

They had their own leavenings, but weren't aware of them; didn't care to know about them and certainly had no intentions of purging them. Kiz had enough of her own problems at this point in time. Not feeling strong enough or wise enough yet to ward off more bad influences, she stayed to herself for awhile.

She knew she didn't know much, but she did realize that by accepting and tolerating everybody and everything we simply were inviting evil in and accommodating it in a gigantic way. We were letting it become part of us. It was rubbing off on us. She also knew she had to become stronger to ward off what was in the world: there was only one path to do that. Pray, read the Bible and learn how to use the armor of God to deflect the fiery darts of the evil one.

> *"Not forsaking the assembling of ourselves together,"*
> *In Hebrews 10:25*

Someone had told Kiz he was a Church hopper. And they said it with contempt. She always saw him as a solid, hard working, devoted man and at the time didn't understand what he was talking about. Now she was pretty sure she did. She felt she was possibly facing the same dilemma he was. She didn't want to leave Churches. It was a very difficult thing to do. She wanted to become fully integrated into the Body of Christ, but certain things she absolutely could not tolerate. She felt forced to leave. Maybe it was because she hadn't reached any stage of maturity yet.

> *"and how thou canst not bear them which are evil: and thou*
> *hast tried them which say they are apostles, and are not,*
> *and hast found them liars:"*
> *In Revelation 2:2*

This brought some comfort to Kizzy. This actually seemed to be a plus in Jesus' Eyes. Why were we, calling ourselves Christians, allowing these kinds of things to happen in our Churches? Blindness and deception maybe. There could be a lot of reasons.

To Kiz, it deeply felt as if we were allowing the evil one to tromp around in the Sacred and Holy Blood that Jesus had shed for us. Making a mockery of everything that the Lord had created and everything He had done for us. She didn't know what to do. It caused her pain, even to the very core of her bones.

> *"For there are certain men crept in unawares, who were*
> *before of old ordained to this condemnation,*
> *ungodly men, turning the Grace of God into*
> *lasciviousness,"*
> *In Jude verse 4*

Did this explain part of it? All of it? What were we to do? Were these people considered our brothers and sisters in Christ? Were they actually part of the Body of Christ? She couldn't believe they were. Kiz had gotten herself in a lot deeper than she ever thought when she prayed that prayer. Little did she know it would get deeper.

She was genuinely disturbed, confused, sick about the whole mess. She fell on the floor in a defeated heap. She cried and prayed. Prayed and cried. And cried and prayed some more. "God what am I to do? How am I to understand? Please God, please, help me."

It felt as if she was trying to be forced to love, accept and tolerate things the Bible rejected. Bad behavior. She felt she was fighting against the whole world. Was this God's Way? Her despair deepened. She didn't want to be of the world anymore. She wanted out.

After what seemed like forever, something stirred in her. Had it been days or weeks? She wasn't sure because she was living in a confused mist. All Kiz was aware of was that she was to get pen, paper, Bible, dictionary, concordance and start writing.

What Lord? Now what?

~II~

If you see a wrong that sickens your soul and affects you in a negative way for an extended period of time, what are you to do?

Give it to You and wait?

What do you see as the difference between justice and vengeance?

I don't know, I'll look.

Justice (Webster's)

1. A being righteous
2. Fairness
3. Rightfulness
4. Reward or penalty as deserved
5. The use of authority to uphold what is just
6. The administration of law

S.S. Riley

Where would this lead? That's all Kiz needed, more questions she didn't have answers for. Maybe she wasn't meant to know. These descriptions sounded good but that presented another, more complex question. According to whose ways? God's Way and man's way were two completely different things. She hadn't met very many people who were looking out for God's Way. And man's way was beginning to get on her last nerve, big time. She desperately needed healing.

Vengeance (Webster's)

1. The return of an injury for an injury, as retribution, revenge
2. With great force or fury
3. Excessively

> *"Vengeance is Mine; I will repay, saith the Lord."*
> *In Romans 12:19*

Kiz thought this was really scary. And knew it was true and would be done. Was it being done now? But how was this helping? She had no intentions of exacting justice or vengeance on anyone. She did, though, want to scream, "WAKE UP! Can't you see what you are doing?" That WOULD be hypocrisy because she had been there. Not doing these kinds of things in a Church, but, well… She had been doing wrong things while claiming to be a Christian. She was just another believer that didn't obey. A believer that really didn't believe enough to follow the rules. Or didn't care about the rules.

> *"Ye have heard that it hath been said, An eye for an eye,*
> *and a tooth for a tooth: But I say unto you, That ye resist*
> *not evil: but whosoever shall smite thee on they right cheek,*
> *turn to him the other also."*
> *Matthew 5:39*

Should this be considered justice or vengeance? She believed it would be vengeance. That was for God alone. If we weren't to resist ALL evil, why would the Bible tell us to put on the armor of God? To protect us? Kiz didn't think this was giving her any answers, but she felt the leading of the Spirit. God was giving her answers and He would make it clear. She decided she better follow along.

"Seeing it is a righteous thing with God to recompense
tribulation to them that trouble you."
2 Thessalonians 1:6

Oh, my gosh! No. If what she thought God was telling her was true, what was she going to do? She didn't have a choice in the matter. She was troubled alright; but she really didn't want bad things to happen. Not to her brothers and sisters that she dearly loved. Not to anyone really. She had probably been recompensed tribulation for trouble she had caused other people.

"And they came to Jerusalem and Jesus went into the temple,
and began to cast out them that sold and bought in the
temple, and overthrew the tables of the money changers,
and the seats of them that sold doves; And would not
suffer (allow) that any man should carry any vessel
(wares) through the temple. And He taught, saying, Is it not
written, My House shall be called of all nations the
House of Prayer? But ye have made it a den of thieves."
Mark 11:15-17

Now Kiz was using every sense she had not to turn any of this to her advantage. She checked her thoughts, prayed and waited for vision. Considering Jesus is to be our role model and we are to pattern our lives after His and follow in His footsteps, is it right for us to also cause upheaval to right a wrong?

"And if any man obey not our word by this epistle,
note that man, and have no company with him,
that he may be ashamed. Yet count him not
as an enemy, but admonish him as a brother."
2 Thessalonians 3:14,15

Kiz looked up "admonish" in Webster's: warn, reprove mildly. Hmm…we were supposed to put the word on them. Would an enemy be considered a brother or sister? The family of Christ? Are all people in the family of Christ as she had been told?

S.S. Riley

"For as many as are led by the Spirit of God, they are the Sons of God. For ye have not received the spirit of bondage again to fear, but ye have received the spirit of adoption, whereby we cry, Abba, Father. The Spirit Itself beareth witness with our spirit, that we are the Children of God."
Romans 8:14-16

"And because ye are sons, God hath sent forth the Spirit of His Son into our hearts, crying, Abba, Father."
Galatians 4:6

"Having predestinated us unto the adoption of children by Jesus Christ to Himself, according to the Good Pleasure of His Will."
Ephesians 1:5

Our adoption is through Jesus Christ. Just because someone believes in God but rejects Jesus, are they our brothers and sisters? Have all people been adopted? Will all people be adopted? Kizzy was being told "no."

"And that we may be delivered from unreasonable and wicked men; for all men have not faith."
2 Thessalonians 3:2

"Now we command you, brethren, in the Name of our Lord Jesus Christ, that ye withdraw yourselves from every brother that walketh disorderly, and not after the tradition which he received of us."
2 Thessalonians 3:6

Yeah, Kiz had withdrawn herself. She felt it was a "must do" thing, but still wasn't sure it was a good thing.

"Men and brethren, this Scripture must needs have been fulfilled, which the Holy Ghost by the mouth of David spoke

before concerning Judas, which was guide to them
that took Jesus."
Acts 1:16

Kiz wondered, if the Holy Ghost spoke through David's mouth and the mouths of the prophets, could and would He still be speaking through people today? She believed it to be so. As she read the verse over and over slowly, hoping for insight, it came. Something caught her attention.

"Men and brethren..." Acts 1:16
"Men and brethren..." Acts 2:29
"...men and brethren..." Acts 2:37
"...men, brethren and fathers... Acts 7:2
"...men and brethren..." Acts 13:15
"Men and brethren..." Acts 13:26
"...men and brethren..." Acts 13:38
"...Men and brethren..." Acts 15:7
"...Men and brethren..." Acts 15:13
"Men, brethren and fathers..." Acts 22:1
"...men and brethren..." Acts 23:1
"...men and brethren..." Acts 23:6
"...men and brethren..." Acts 28:17

Kiz thought she remembered that the book of Acts was written by Luke. She pondered, then prayed. Why had the Spirit shown her that thirteen times while with groups of people, he made this very clear distinction? Or had Paul made the division? She didn't know. But it had become clear to her that, no, we were not all brothers and sisters in the Body of Christ.

"While I was with them in the world, I kept them in Thy Name;
those that Thou gavest Me I have kept,
and none of them was lost, but the son of perdition;
that the Scripture might be fulfilled."
John 17:12

She looked up perdition in Webster's: hell, the loss of the soul. A footnote in her Bible said destruction. Yes, Judas was the son of perdition.

*"But Godliness with contentment is great gain. For we
brought nothing into this world, and it is certain we can
carry nothing out. And having food and raiment
let us therewith be content. But they that will be
rich fall into temptation and a snare, and into
many hurtful and foolish lusts, which drown men in
destruction and perdition."*
1 Timothy 6:6-9

*"Now the just shall live by faith: but if any man draw
back, my soul shall have no pleasure in him, But we
are not of them who draw back into perdition; but of them
that believe to the saving of the soul."*
Hebrews 10:38,39

Is that what was happening in the Churches? People drawing back into perdition? Thinking all was well when it really wasn't? Fear and dread, almost panic stiffened her. She began to pray. A flood of relief washed over her as the Words: "return to Me and I will return to you," floated into her mind. There was hope. If the Lord had gotten through her thick, numb skull, He could get through anyone's. She continued praying for an awakening in the Body.

*"But the heavens and the earth, which are now, by the same
Word are kept in store, reserved unto fire against the day of
judgment and perdition of ungodly men."*
2 Peter 2:3

During her search of the concordance looking for verses she was being led to, she noticed that the word "perdition" was not in the Old Testament, only in the New Testament. Also, it appeared that the word "justice" was only in the Old Testament, not in the New Testament. Maybe she was mistaken and had missed something. She would recheck later. Right now she felt as if her questions were being answered by the Word.

One of the twelve was a son of perdition. She was finding out that sons of perdition were in the Churches today. Could the ratio possibly be the same? She hoped not. It crossed her mind that they were alive and well, (worldly speaking), and thriving in every area of her life. She decided she needed to stay alert at all times.

"For such are false apostles, deceitful workers, transforming themselves into apostles of Christ...in perils among false brethren."
In 2 Corinthians 11:13,26

"And that because of false brethren unawares brought in, who come in privily to spy out our liberty which we have in Christ Jesus, that they might bring us into bondage."
Galatians 2:4

Yep, Kiz could see that happening all over the place. Mostly in government. But she refused to join in on leader bashing because she knew that they were put in place by God. He was in control, even if things appeared to be quite a mess.

"Beware of false prophets, who come to you in sheep's clothing, but inwardly they are ravening wolves."
Matthew 7:15

"And many false prophets shall rise, and shall deceive many... For there shall arise false christs, and false prophets, and shall shew great signs and wonders, insomuch that, if it were possible, they shall deceive the very elect."
Matthew 24:11,29

Yep again. Kiz was becoming very aware of it. She found out that she hadn't been far off the mark. She chalked it up to discernment, listening to what feelings the Spirit placed in her. We had been programmed to believe that all people are good and mean well. It was a lie. They aren't. We seem to believe just about anything we are told and many of those things are Biblically untrue.

Kiz had come to face the fact that the Bible is our Handbook so graciously supplied by our Creator. The answers are there, you only had to want to find them. It was important to not only read It, but to study It thoroughly and grasp firmly to what It tells us. Otherwise we become just like the unbelieving world. Just like the secular world. Only we don't know it.

One of the untrue things we have been told and believe is that when we see sinful behavior and evil actions we should just love the person. That's what Christians do, love the unlovable. Let them be and just love them. Everything will be okay. No, it won't. Not unless the Spirit makes it okay. It is more than likely Satan is at work in their lives. Not God. More people are going to be lost than saved.

As Kiz mulled over these things in her mind while at work, she could vaguely feel something starting to form on the edges of her brain. When she got home she lowered herself to the floor and cleared her head of everything. Slowly it came. She thanked God and went to her concordance. After a few minutes she found the verse she was looking for:

> *"Then Peter took Him, and began to rebuke Him, saying,*
> *Be it far from Thee Lord: this shall not be unto Thee.*
> *But He turned, and said unto Peter, Get thee behind Me, Satan:*
> *thou art an offence unto Me: for thou savourest not the things*
> *that be of God, but those that be of man."*
> *Matthew 16:22,23*

Of course Kiz looked up "rebuke." The only dictionary she owned was Webster's New World. To scold in a sharp way, reprimand. She had to smile that Peter would speak to the Son of God in that tone of voice. But that's not what upset Jesus. She knew Jesus loved Peter, but what kind of love was He showing here? Hmm…then it came to her. Godly love. Perfect love. Unlike anything we could ever understand and weren't supposed to use in this world. We had so mangled and twisted God's Love that it actually seemed cruel.

In today's world, that kind of love would warrant the term "abuse." That definitely was a no-no. Love as it existed today was right out of Satan's little bag of tricks. If we objected to someone's behavior, we didn't love them. Go ahead and do it, I love you. Kiz smiled at the thought that crossed her mind. Maybe what they really needed was a good swift kick in the pants.

She went back to the concordance and studied what was under "rebuke." For all forms of rebuke there were seventy five entries. They began in Genesis and ended in Revelation. Kiz picked out a few from the New Testament thinking they might be more relevant.

"Them that sin rebuke before all, that others also
may fear."
1 Timothy 5:21

"Preach the Word, be instant in season, out of season; reprove,
rebuke, exhort with all long suffering and doctrine."
2 Timothy 4:2

"Take heed to yourselves; If thy brother trespass against thee,
rebuke him; and if he repent, forgive him."
(Jesus speaking) Luke 17:3

A conversation with a certain preacher came to mind. What if, when rebuked, our brother becomes obstinate, rude, defensive and insulting. He hasn't repented. Are we required to forgive then? Is it in our best interest to forgive anyway? If we skip the rebuking part altogether, are we being disobedient? Jesus did tell us to do it. Do we just stand idly by and let our brethren spiral out of control? Go backwards into perdition?

Could it be that doing nothing meant we were letting evil into ourselves? Do we want children who witness the trespass to think it is okay and begin to emulate it? That's what Satan would have us do. But what about God? If Jesus really meant what He said, (and Kiz believed He did,) was it Biblically possible for a Christian to be kind at all times? Kizzy voted "no." We had many responsibilities we were neglecting.

Kiz noticed that not all four of the Gospels had rebuke in them. It was omitted from John. The very definition of rebuke: to scold in a sharp way, reprimand, brought to her mind a certain level of anger. When Jesus rebuked evil spirits and they obeyed, she couldn't envision Him saying something like, "Oh, you guys, you better come out now, won't you please?"

She started perusing the concordance again. The word "anger" was listed eighty-seven times, "anger of the Lord" - eighteen times, "In anger" - thirty-three, "anger kindled" - thirty-six times, "slow to anger" - eight times "provoke" or "provoked to anger" - forty-four times, "anger" - one time, "angry" - forty-three times.

That sounded like an awful lot of anger. God got angry and Kiz dreaded the culmination of His Anger as it was revealed in Revelation. Jesus got angry when he walked this earth. There was no Commandment that said "thou shalt not get angry."

Jesus became angry many times, but He did not sin. Could there really be such a thing as justifiable anger? How about "righteous indignation?" Righteous indignation could not serve our own self-interests. If it didn't serve the Lord, it was something else. Sin maybe?

Are we passionate about the Word of God and about keeping His Body Holy, Pure and Righteous? We are His Body and it is riddled with evil. So...we should be, (we better be.) We are surrendering to evil by letting it slide, by allowing it to grow strong, sturdy roots. By trying to follow the world's path to political correctness.

> *"Be angry, and sin not:*
> *let not the sun go down upon your wrath;"*
> *Ephesians 4:26*

Kiz took from this that she should get over it or take care of the problem as soon as possible. She couldn't stop the sun from going down. If Jesus was frequently angry with the world, but did not sin, how did He do it? Was it easy for Him because He is God? Maybe not. Kiz went into blank mind, silent mode. Then, there it was!

> *"Casting down imaginations, and every high thing that*
> *exalted itself against the knowledge of God, and*
> *bringing into captivity every thought to the*
> *obedience of Christ."*
> *2 Corinthians 10:5*

Her mind had a tendency to wander quite frequently. Often to places it should-n't be. One way Kiz found to control part of this was to begin looking in the Bible for answers to things that bothered her. She found that her mind would then dwell on what she had read rather than the problem itself. Plus, she actually wanted to obey the Lord now. It wasn't easy, but she was trying.

While she continued slowly contemplating verses in the New Testament that contained the word "rebuke," this one opened her eyes.

> *"And one of the malefactors which were hanged railed on Him,*
> *saying, If Thou be Christ, save Thyself and us.*
> *But the other answering rebuked him, saying,*
> *Dost not thou fear God,*
> *seeing thou art in the same condemnation?*
> *And we justly; for we receive the due reward of our deeds;*
> *but This Man hath done nothing amiss.*
> *And he said unto Jesus, Lord, remember me when Thou comest*
> *into Thy Kingdom. And Jesus said unto him,*
> *Verily I say unto thee, today thou shalt be with Me in Paradise."*
> Luke 23:39-43

That brought to mind:

> *"And will shew mercy on whom I will shew mercy."*
> In Exodus 33:19

She had read that passage in Luke lots of times before, but apparently had not understood it. The word "railed" should give us a clue. The man was probably terrified and screaming, using any logic he could think of to get himself out of this most horrid, shameful death.

Kiz was sure words weren't used haphazardly in the Bible. If It says "rebuked," It means rebuked or some other softer word would have been used. Like maybe admonished.

Jesus didn't say, "Now, now, you yelled at that other guy, that's a no-no." He said, "To day you shall be with Me in Paradise." That was after He said believe and be baptized and you will be saved. The second man surely hadn't been baptized, but he seemed to believe.

She was led to Titus.

> *"To speak evil to no man, to be no brawlers, but gentle,*
> *shewing meekness unto all men."*
> *Titus 3:2*

She read further.

> *"A man that is an heretick after the first and second admonition,*
> *reject; Knowing that he that is such is subverted, and sinneth,*
> *Being condemned of himself."*
> *Titus 3:10,11*

What? Maybe we made a mistake! Reject someone? Well! Isn't that politically incorrect! How dare we?

> *"For there are many unruly and vain talkers and deceivers,*
> *specially they of the circumcision: Whose mouth must be stopped,*
> *who subvert whole houses, teaching things which they ought not,*
> *for filthy lucre's sake. One of themselves, even a prophet*
> *of their own, said, The Cretans are always liars, evil beasts,*
> *slowbellies. This witness is true. Wherefore rebuke them*
> *sharply, that they may be sound in the faith."*
> *Titus 1:10-13*

So...Titus is supposed to set the Church in good working order and strengthen the faith. But they are what? Liars? Evil beasts? Slowbellies? Is it love to speak such things? The truth?

> *"Who gave Himself for us, that He might redeem us from all*
> *iniquity and purify unto Himself a peculiar people,*
> *zealous of good works."*
> *Titus 2:14*

Kiz believed that harsh rebukes would be part of the purification process. Rejecting someone might cause shame and embarrassment and make that person rethink their actions which would be a step closer to purification.

> *"Give not that which is holy unto the dogs, neither cast your*
> *pearls before swine, lest they trample them under*
> *their feet, and turn again and rend you."*
> *Matthew 7:6*

Oh my! Was Jesus calling people dogs and swine? She believed He was. How un-Christian like is that? She'd like to see that happen in this day and age.

> *"If it be possible, as much as it lieth with you,*
> *live peaceably with all men."*
> *Romans 12:18*

If it be possible. Kiz didn't hear it say "do it at all costs." She pulled out that you are to do it as much as it depends on you.

If it is the hottest part of summer with the temperatures hovering right around ninety degrees for days on end and you notice that three days ago your neighbor tied his dog out in the back yard in the sun and still hasn't brought out food and water dishes, do we remain meek and mild? Still living in peace with all men? If we choose to mind our own business, we are as guilty in the dog's suffering as the neighbor. Is there a righteous indignation confrontation in order? Kiz believed there was.

God uses men in His Master Plan.

He used Deborah to encourage Barak. She went into battle with him to keep encouraging him. The foot soldiers won a victorious battle over horses and chariots because of her trust in the Lord.

David was a child. He was too young for war so he was left behind to watch the sheep. Yet the Lord used him to kill the giant, Goliath. David went on to become a great king.

Moses was spared because his mother put him into a basket in the river. He killed an Egyptian that was abusing a Hebrew slave. Yet the Lord used him to bring His people out of captivity.

He used Esther to save her people from annihilation.

He used Ruth as an example that loyalty and hard work will be repaid. She was in the lineage of Christ.

He used righteous Noah and his family to repopulate the world after ALL OTHER MEN were completely wiped out. This included women and children.

Jesus, intending to use people, made disciples.

A chill of excitement and anticipation ran through Kiz's body. Was the Lord preparing her to be used in some way? Was He wanting to use all believers in an important way, but we wouldn't let Him? Were we refusing His call? Had we been so watered down by the world that we had no backbone left for Jesus?

Kiz wanted to become strong in the Lord, confident that He was with her and willing to fight in any battle that He asked of her.

Kiz again went into silent mode.

Getting into Heaven seemed somewhat comparable to getting into a sold out concert or sports event. There was only one way in. Be on intimate terms with someone on the inside. In Heaven's case, that meant Jesus. That required obedience. Was everyone going to make it? She sure hoped so.

She prayed a solemn prayer of thanksgiving for answers to a multitude of things that had been plaguing her for years. She was relieved that she didn't have to swallow down all of the tolerance and acceptance people were trying to spoon feed her. She was relieved she didn't have to feel bad because it made her angry at times. The Lord had finally given her peace on THAT front, but she still had a long way to go.

Chapter 16

"though Thou tookest vengeance of their inventions."
In Psalm 99:8

"Thus they provoked Him to anger with their inventions…
Thus were they defiled with their own works, and
went a whoring with their own inventions."
In Psalm 106:29, 39

"Lo, this only have I found, that God hath made man
upright, but they have sought out many inventions."
Ecclesiastes 7:29

Hey Paul, is this a bad time?

Not at all, have a seat. Ironically it seems I was doing this exact same thing last time you stopped by.

Going through files.

Yep.

Paper files.

How astute of you to notice.

With all of this technology, why paper files?

Because I want things to be kept confidential. No one needs to know who comes to see me. My clients deserve at least that much.

Thank you.

For what?

Realizing it. Most people don't.

What's on your mind today?

Those, to start.

Paper files?

Yeah. What happened, Paul?

You didn't give me enough information to answer that question. I could begin on any number of topics.

Oh, sorry.

Don't be sorry, you usually start out slow and WHAM! You bring out the big guns.

You want the big guns first?

Not really. You make me think. Then I pretty much have it figured out about the time the bomb goes off.

How do you picture Eve in the Garden of Eden?

I'm thinking.

Thought I smelled smoke.

Funny. Like I never heard that one before.

So?

I don't know yet. Perfect? Is that it?

Partly. But perfect in whose eyes?

God's definitely. Adam's. Weren't many around to notice.

Precisely. Want to know what I think?

Go on.

Eve probably had dirt on her. Being in a garden and all. Mud between her toes. Dirt under her nails. Hair a tangled mess, probably with leaves and stuff in it. Hair growing in places we think of as disgusting today, places God meant for hair to grow. Can you picture it?

Never thought about it but now that you bring it up, yes. I can.

When Jesus said you must come to Him as a child would be, that's what I see. A messy little kid. Dirt on her face. Smiling. Innocent. Oblivious to the fact that she is a mess and really doesn't care.

And we've gotten so sophisticated. I agree, but try as I might, it's not fitting in with paper files.

Oh, but if my thinking is correct, it will.

Go on.

Laney asked her mother for razors and lotion so she could have long, smooth, silky legs.

She's what, nine or ten now?

Thirteen.

Yes, time flies doesn't it? Did she get them?

No. And you'll never guess what she did get.

Haven't a clue.

In the end, a big bonfire.

You'll explain, I hope.

Oh yes, that's why I'm here. We sat her down and talked to her. Because woman was the original sinner that made her the perfect target. Since there really is no perfect woman, women have become victims of demands. The world is trying to make us believe there is perfection in physical beauty. But what God wants is inner beauty. Our minds are warped. We love our temptations, we don't flee from them. We strive to make them more and more appealing. Men are the worst because they expect what they see advertised.

Excuse me?

In general, Paul, the world. You know what I mean.

Yes, that's why I try to be an exception.

Thank you for that. Well, what we tried to explain to her was that no one was happy with the way things are. They want more, improved, better. They will pay any price to attain it. Even roasting in hell.

How did she take that?

Not well, I'm afraid. She was angry. We tried to explain that evil seeds of destruction had been planted. They were being taken very seriously and caused a lot of grief and financial problems.

And she was agreeable?

No. She called us hypocrites.

Whoa! And?

We agreed.

She thought she was getting her way then?

Maybe for a second. Then came the bonfire.

You walked away from an important discussion to have a bonfire? Was it to continue the conversation in a different atmosphere?

You could look at it that way if you want. I remembered the Bible said even to look on vanity was a sin. I walked away carrying a TV set. My wife walked away carrying a game system. Laney walked away carrying magazines and her cell phone.

In the bonfire?

Yep, all of it. It made me sick when Laney showed me pictures friends had sent to her of their long, smooth, silky legs. Naked all the way up to their crotch with just their underwear on. That was the final straw. Computers, printers, wires, remotes, the whole shebang.

Wow. That's a lot of toxins being released into the air. I'm surprised you did it that way.

I figured God would forgive me just this once. The way I see it, it's a lot better than all of the other toxins they are releasing.

Yes…all of that radiation and microwaves and…

Not that. I'm talking about smut. What we see and hear. None of it can be taken back from our minds and it keeps resurfacing any time it feels like it.

We got rid of everything that advertises. I guess to make a final point to Laney, the last thing my wife threw on the fire was her razor and lotion. She had a smirk of a look on her face like, you just wait buddy.

Good last point.

Have you ever watched shows for kids?

Yeah, when my grandkids come over. Witches, warlocks, magic wands, time travel, magic. It's pretty graphic, especially the violence. Then there are the ones that concentrate on butts and passing gas. We don't turn it on anymore.

It's the easy road to sin and temptation. Pointing our minds in disgusting directions. You don't even have to leave your couch to be enticed or immersed in it. It's right there in our hands. Twenty-four hours a day. We aren't even safe in our own homes. Evil flying at us from every direction. How much more sinister can it get? All under the guise of information, education and entertainment.

I see your point. It's crossed my mind more than a few times.

You know what else bugs me?

I believe I'm going to find out.

Weather forecasting and astrology. Doesn't the Bible warn us to stay away from stuff like that? My secretary plans her day by what her astrology reading says. It's the first thing she does every morning. I quit bringing the paper to work.

Isn't she a Christian?

Yeah. That's where I see the problem. I've talked to her about it, but she laughs and waves me off. She says it's harmless, all in fun. And it's December. Don't you expect it will probably be cold and might snow? Are we so stupid we need someone to tell us that? What is our problem?

You sound annoyed.

I am. A little. I listen to the morning show on the Christian radio station on my way to work. Well, I used to. The morning host talks nonstop about sports. And he gets so excited about it. He knows everything about every player and every statistic that was ever in existence. It sounds like he never misses a game. How much time do you think all of that takes? It bothers me. How is any of that furthering the cause of Christ?

It isn't.

Another thing that's bothering me is this free-phone business. It seems that I'm accosted from all sides every time I try to go into a store. "Did you sign up for your free phone yet?" I always tell them nothing is free. Someone, somewhere is paying dearly for it. There's invisible strings attached, no thanks. I would rather work for what I have. You'll be sorry when the government goes belly-up and the Chinese move in and take over. I've been called quite a few choice things. Mostly "weirdo".

And you aren't?

I am. To the world I guess. We're supposed to be in the world, not of the world. All of this technology is evil. I don't believe God is happy that we so lovingly embrace it. Yeah, I own it. I'm a weirdo. There are just too many temptations we shouldn't be subjecting ourselves to.

Or our kids. They need to be taught right from wrong. How is Laney taking it?

She was good and mad for the first two weeks. We told her it was okay to be mad. Eventually she would understand. Don't know if that's what calmed her down, but something did. She's finding out who her real friends are. You know she's taken up baking and knitting? She helps around the house without being asked, she started doing her own laundry and her room is spotless. We aren't all separated, doing our own device thing. It's turning out to be what I always thought a home should be.

She bakes?

Yeah. We told her she couldn't always make junk food, she has to get some nutrition into the stuff. Now we get carrot cake, zucchini bread, apple pie, pumpkin cookies. It's great.

I'll have to stop over.

Please do. There's always something there now and she would be happy to share. In fact, she sent you some banana bread.

Couldn't be happier. Thanks. But...paper files? I have a feeling you're getting to something a little more serious here.

Yeah...I'd like to, but I'm not sure where to start?

Complicated?

Oh my, yes.

How about we start with the WHAM and work back from there.

Okay. I believe the mark of the beast is being put in place as we speak.

You don't say. I never expected that.

So go backwards?

Please do.

The idols we worship eventually make slaves of us. Technology is one of the biggest idols we worship. The list is long, but that's right at the top.

I'm getting the idea. Tell me what you think.

Evil usually starts out small. Say 78 RPM's. That's all it is. Just music in the house. Then we advance. We go to 33 1/3rd, then 45's. Just music in the house. Then we advance more. A little transistor radio, 8 tracks, cassettes, CD's, digital. So, as it progresses, we create a great deal of stuff that becomes useless. Trash. The music advances slowly, too, until it's basically trash. Look at some of the stuff we have today. Horrifying stuff. Kill people and then write songs about it. Beat the woman and kids and write songs about that. Sing about rape, drugs, alcohol and prostitutes. Then become millionaires. Look at the thousands of dollars we invest in advanced sound systems. We don't screen what our kids listen to. Even if you try, they get it from their friends. We're glorifying evil and paying huge money to do it. You let a little evil in and Satan kicks the door wide open.

So you think all music is evil?

Lately, yes. When you're using expensive technology and doing it for fame, ego and money, yes. It's evil.

I agree. I've been seeing elaborate entertainment centers in people's homes. They look like altars to technology and entertainment.

They are altars.

We are worshipping it, aren't we? But you've started at the beginning. We were supposed to work our way backwards.

Yes. The mark of the beast. Chips, Paul, microchips. We're using them in our pets, and insanely scared to death parents are using either cell phones to track their kids or attaching chips to them in case they get lost or stolen. They track their every move.

Parentnoid.

What?

New word some of us made up. Parentnoid.

So true. I wouldn't put it past authorities to be doing it to us right now.

Without our knowledge?

Please.

Yeah, huh.

We've got our kids so excited about stuff, that's all they think about. How much stuff they have and how much more stuff they can't live without. There's always more stuff, constant upgrades and improvements that keep us in bondage mentally and financially. They are a huge distraction from the truth. Nobody wants to talk about that anymore. They just want to talk about stuff. We're in really big trouble here.

So we start small with chips in our animals and when that becomes old hat, we upgrade. We advance.

Exactly. But we advance to where? How far is Satan going to take us.? To the mark of the beast. His mark. As far as we let him take us. You mark my words, it's going to be the ruin of us. A one-way ticket to hell.

The technology or the worshipping of it?

Both. Everything resulting from it is of the beast. It is oppressing us little by little, step-by-step. Now, with this whole healthcare thing being crammed down our throats, I believe the next step will be microchips being forced on us. Right hand or forehead? That way our whole medical record will be carried with us at all times. In a wreck? Unconscious? ID can't be found? Tired of filling out all of that bothersome paperwork? Here, the modern miracles of our time will make things so much easier... and safer.

That's where the paper files come in! I see. You know they're micro-chipping people in Sweden already. I think they started about ten years ago, but I'm not sure. Medical and financial information ready at your service.

They're doing it here in the U.S., too. A lot closer than Sweden. What scares me is that there won't even be any kind of warning or announcement made declaring what it is. You think somebody is going to say, "Come get the mark of the beast!" It will all be put in place gradually. One store will ask if you have the chip. Get our app. We're all about apps. We'll scan you, you get the store discounts and pay all at the same time. Quick, easy, painless. How convenient is that? Then more and more places will conform. Bureau of Motor Vehicles, library, police departments, utility companies. Eventually you won't be able to buy anything without it. Man, it's scary.Doesn't it say in the Bible that we will believe what's good is evil and what's evil is good?

I couldn't tell you for sure. I believe it is, but where, I have no idea.

Knowledge of evil seems to be overtaking knowledge of good. It's my firm belief that if we don't have a chip, first we won't be able to buy or pay for ANYTHING and then later, it will be used to identify that we don't have one. If we don't, we will be persecuted.

How will they know who has one and who doesn't?

Technology. There are drones everywhere. You think they couldn't scan a person on the ground to see whether they're chipped or not? And eventually I think those drones will be armed. Things are going into place quickly. We're headed for big trouble whether you get the chip or not.

They find the chip and know you're marked. My gut is telling me it's true, but do you know how this is going to sound to the general public?

The ones that thrive on all the stuff and shop three or four times a day? Like hogwash. Like a conspiracy theory. Like whoever thought of it was out of their gourd. There are lots and lots of warnings in the Bible, but people don't even read much of it anymore. We're blinded by stuff. Nobody really takes it seriously. It's like some kind of fairy tale. They're stuck on the love part. Too much other stuff to occupy their minds.

Occupy. Live in. Hmm...The Lord sent us into the world with one cord. When that was cut, it should have been the end of it. Look what we've done. Strangled ourselves with so many cords it isn't even funny. No freedom in that. We've become slaves to the stuff. We don't need to put it in drive. We need to slam on the brakes and back it up.

I've been feeling lately like we're paving the way for the beast. The golden road of sin and excess ushering him in. And Christians are up to their necks in it. That's another scary part. Jesus tells us that many will be called but few chosen. I wonder what He means by few and chosen for what? If the microchip IS the mark of the beast, what do you think He will do with all of His followers who clamored to get it so they could buy, buy, buy?

The Bible says that whoever gets it will burn and the smoke of them will be seen forever. Something like that, don't quote me on it.

I won't, I'll look it up. Even if we had no idea what we were getting ourselves into? Burn?

We will probably be warned not to get it by that small, still voice. The Spirit will probably give us fair warning. Who will heed that voice? Who will ignore it and get the pass to buy anyway? It scares me.

Everyone that is of the truth heareth My Voice." Or something like that.

So we hear it and do what we want anyway. Makes me shiver.

Me, too.

I hope you aren't asking me to do any research on this, because it can't be researched.

I know. Smart move, huh? Leave no evidence.

The mark is evidence enough. You can't escape the All Knowing Creator.

But can the All Knowing Creator escape you?

Good question. I'll bet He can. Hey, I just had a thought.

S.S. Riley

Oh, yeah? Another one?

Yep. God is All Knowing and Satan isn't. Yet he wants to be above God or His equal in all things. You think maybe he has everyone stockpiling every bit of information they can get so he will know it all? Like stores keeping track of every single thing you buy with a card? Everything is in computers now. Could that be like Satan's nerve center? Social websites, texting, emails. People tell all on those things. About themselves and everybody they know. No dirt is hidden. You think he would do that?

He'll never have God's Knowledge, Wisdom or Understanding, but yes, I think he is trying to reach that perfection. Whatever it takes. He will never make it, though. You think you've erased all of that garbage, but it's still out there. Someone can always go back and find it. That stuff isn't gone like you think it is. Like Laney's friend's legs and crotch. That plan is very possible because Satan is imperfect. I wonder if he has memory problems. Always trying to be above God.

It won't happen, he's already beaten. Why do you think he keeps trying so hard?

His nature. Pure evil.

And he wants to take as many of us with him as he can. Hey, I'd best be getting out of here. It's later than I thought. Sorry to have kept you so long. Thanks for the talk, it's always enlightening even if it sometimes is frightening.

You're welcome and I think you're right about the mark of the beast. A microchip conveniently in a person would be a treasure trove in the wrong hands. Plus, where else is technology taking us?

Or in the hands of a demon.

Tell Laney the banana bread was fantastic. I've eaten the whole thing.

I noticed.

Chapter 17

"to every man that is among you, not to think of himself
more highly than he ought to think;"
In Romans 12:3

Once again the yearning and deep need to be among fellow believers haunted Kiz. She started searching. Anything. Anywhere, but one of "those" Churches. Well, not anything. It had to be a Christian, Bible-based Church. Kiz had passed a Church not far from her home many times, but it looked kind of dead. Nothing ever seemed to be happening there and the sign out front almost never changed. It wasn't one of "those" Churches, so she decided to try it.

She walked in that first Sunday morning with her eyes, ears and heart wide open and on high alert. One woman greeted her with a hearty hello, a big smile, but no one else spoke to her.

Kiz was tingling from head to toe. She thought of it as the Movement of the Spirit. Was it the Church or was it just within her? She decided to wait a good long time before making that decision. She had been lambasted enough as it was. Her expectations didn't run high.

The service was beautiful, except for the music: contemporary and played very loudly on electrical instruments. So loudly in fact that you couldn't hear any voices except the ones with microphones. It was only a personal choice, but she didn't care for a rock band in a Church. She knew not one of the songs and the words were flashed on a screen. She thought contemporary Christian songs belonged on a radio, not in a service. They were written by professional singers for professional singers.

As she looked around, she noticed most of the people fidgeting, messing with their phones and not singing. She couldn't hold a note for sixty eight seconds and wondered if the row of elderly women in front of her could. Probably not. Singing the same three lines over and over felt to her as if there was a lack of talent and feeling for the Lord.

But...only God knew their hearts and she didn't want to be judgmental. She couldn't sing along, she tried but there was no genuine feeling in it. She waited like most of the rest. She would try to live with the music even though she wasn't a professional singer. She longed to be belting out some old hymns accompanied by a piano or organ. She longed to hear the voices of her brothers and sisters being raised to the Creator.

After going back a few times and finding nothing that was offensive to her in the way of worship, she started volunteering for different things and asked where help was needed.

She started to notice that most of the people seemed to belong to cliques. It reminded her so much of high school, one of the reasons she had quit going. If you didn't fit in with a certain group or any of the groups, you were on your own.

Kiz couldn't say that about ALL of the folks, but the biggest majority had settled in amongst friends and there didn't seem to be any general acceptance of a new person. She was nice to everyone, but felt a wall if it could be described as that. Definitely a dividing line.

Even Bible study classes before services were divided. There was a class for each clique and Kiz chose the one the pastor's mother led. She was a delightful elderly woman. The class eventually came to, well, maybe not accept Kiz fully, but she felt tolerated.

"run not with them to the same excess."
In 1 Peter 4:4

Boy, this Church liked to eat. Kizzy attended several feasts after services. The hospitality committee kept themselves busy. She believed this is what Jesus meant by breaking bread and pouring wine. "Do this in remembrance of Me." There was no wine, of course. Communion with fellow believers. Eating together, being together. But it kept on. Lots and lots of huge meals, feeding themselves.

Kiz was becoming uncomfortable. She felt in her heart that if this much money, time and food was spent feeding the vast number of homeless and poverty stricken in the city, they might possibly, maybe, be approaching doing a good thing. But they didn't. It was all within the Church, all for them.

At the last get-together she attended, one of the elders wouldn't eat. He was complaining about how much money was being spent on food. She silently agreed. She didn't leave the Church, but she did withdraw herself from the feasts.

"Their strength is to sit still..."
In Isaiah 30:7

One of the talents the Lord had blessed her with was handwork; knit and crochet - working with yarn, turning it into usable items. She had been making hats and scarves for the homeless for quite some time and thought there might be some people in the Church who would like to make it a project as well. She approached the pastor, who ran it by the elders. It was okayed and became a real ministry.

Several women came to the first few meetings. One woman asked around the retirement home she lived in. Bags and bags of yarn were donated. Kiz offered to teach these skills and reported to the elders every month how many hats and scarves were turned in.

As with most things, after a while it began to lose steam. So Kiz asked the pastor if maybe they could put on a short fashion type show to thank donors and participants and maybe put a little interest back into "project yarn." He seemed excited and said he would check his sermons to see which it would fit with best.

Kiz waited and waited. At least two months had gone by. She was sure she would have heard something by now. She went back to the pastor to remind him. He informed her that he did not like the idea one bit. He didn't want anyone show-boating and his services were going to be more serious, more holy, more God centered. He didn't think a fashion show was going to fit in anywhere.

She mentioned the chef that put on skits during services for the cooking classes the Church had. She was told that Chef Basil had been doing it since the classes started and would continue. Some people were just angry because their ministries didn't get as much attention as others.

Kiz was a little stunned. There wasn't an angry bone in her body about it. The project and fashion show had been okayed by the elders and now he was shutting it down. No problem. She totally agreed that more attention should be put on the Lord and accepted it at that.

She left without staying for the big Fourth-of-July bash that was being held in the parking lot. She noticed a few angry faces at the edges of the crowd. The same ones that didn't think the Church should be spending so much money on food and parties. She drove home humming, looking forward to a much deeper worship of her beloved Savior the next week.

She went straight to the sanctuary on Sunday to prepare for worship. She meditated on the big wooden cross. As the music started and people were asked to come for worship, Kiz was dumbfounded to see a laughing woman approach the microphone. She started to announce winners for the best patriotic costumes at the party last week.

Kiz was aware that her eyebrows were raised but couldn't find the presence of mind to lower them. This surely wasn't what she expected. What was going on? Elaborate gift baskets were awarded to the winners. The congregation erupted into applause and laughter. Maybe the pastor just didn't like her. She bore no grudges. She was surprised by the lie, but didn't take it personally. For her own sake, she forgave and let it go.

Kiz said nothing about it and let the mission gradually fail. She was sure the Lord had His reasons. One bright spot lightened her days. She had made what she believed to be a good friend. An English lady that loved to knit.

They continued on with their work, branching out to make what her friend called lap rugs. Small blankets they took to a nursing home at Christmastime for people who got no visitors. It certainly wasn't much, but it was something.

"Bear ye one another's burdens…"
In Galatians 6:2

Kizzy's youngest daughter was on her third deployment with the National Guard. Her first was to Iraq, then Kuwait. Now she was in Afghanistan. There was serious trouble brewing. A young soldier had gone into a village and shot several Afghans. While burning what they thought was trash, someone noticed Korans in the flames. It was a hard, dangerous time.

Kiz was soaring. Not with arms outstretched, but more like an eagle that was diving. Arms beside her. She could see mountainous desert terrain with a dirt road beneath her. There was a convoy of tanker trucks off in the distance moving slowly, raising huge clouds of dust. They came single file, closer and closer.

She couldn't seem to control her flight. All of a sudden she zoomed in a loop, diving, coming to a dead stop in a huge silver pipe under the road. There was something cylindrical in there, wrapped in a rough brown cloth. Burlap maybe. Was it a body? No, it was too perfectly round to be a body. A leg? No, it was bigger than a leg.

As Kiz realized it was a bomb, an IED, the trucks rumbled overhead. She was blinded by a bright orange explosion. Kiz woke up sobbing, screaming her daughter's name over and over.

Kiz always gave her daughter over to the Lord when she was deployed. There was no sense in worrying. A year was a long time to keep yourself paralyzed with fear. If something happened, well, she would somehow deal with it then with the Lord's help. He would see her through.

The dream caused her to become extremely distraught. She prayed and asked the Lord for peace. It was only a dream, but still, it took quite a while to get herself settled down. It wasn't like here; she couldn't just pick up the phone and call. She would have to wait.

The next day she was at the Church to help with something and decided to speak with the preacher. Maybe they could pray for her daughter together. Kiz related the dream to him and admitted how badly it had upset her.

She couldn't be absolutely sure, but it seemed like he was making fun of her. Leaning forward with his elbows on his knees, wringing his hands in mock anxiety, talking about what would he do if his heart went out. It was all very strange. There was no prayer except as Kiz was walking away. She was praying for him.

Her daughter called a week later. All was fine and she loved her mother very much.

"Behold, I know your thoughts…"
In Job 21:27

Some of the elders and leaders were out of town one Sunday. The congregation was informed that they were interviewing a young man that looked rather promising as a new worship leader. Kiz was hoping he would be a somewhat more traditional type.

Word soon came that he had been hired and was on his way with his wife.

Her hopes were dashed the Sunday he led his first service. It was more of the same only louder and more repetitive. As time progressed it only increased in volume until you couldn't think. Many complaints were made. People were basically told to pipe down. It wasn't any of their business. They hadn't hired him.

Yes, Kizzy thought. We didn't have a choice in the matter, but it was our tithes and offerings that were paying his salary and buying all of the expensive equipment he claimed the Church needed. Dissatisfaction grew among the ranks.

S.S. Riley

Even the old hymns he did play were so distorted and modernized they were unrecognizable. Just extremely loud noise.

If God could read our every silent thought, what was the need for this? Older people stopped coming. Soon an announcement was made that there would be auditions for a Gospel choir. Several people tried out, but no one ever heard anything. Not a word. That excitement died on the vine.

No gospel choir materialized and some of the elders were complaining about the huge sums of money he was investing to upgrade the systems. Kiz wondered who was running the Church. His solos increased and grew louder. Other band members stood idle while he performed. A lot of the songs he had written himself. It appeared he must be on some kind of ego trip or something.

He started taking up more and more time that should have been devoted to worship until there was literally a forty-five minute rock concert every Sunday morning, starring him.

Most of the congregation was extremely unhappy about it, but nothing was done. He seemed to have free reign to do whatever he wanted.

> *"Having then gifts differing according to the grace that*
> *is given to us…"*
> *In Romans 12:6*

Kiz was told that the missions board would have members present ideas and then vote on what they would like to do. Since she wanted to be more deeply involved in community, she decided to go to see what kinds of things she could help with. Her heart belonged to the community, particularly with the homeless and poor. There was a great need and she was hungering to help fill it. Maybe this was the ticket.

The pastor led the meeting in his loud, boisterous way. He started by going around the table, asking each person for their suggestions on the next mission. There were a lot of great ideas. Kiz was getting excited; finally something worthwhile. The good works we were saved to do. But…it wasn't going to happen.

When it got to be the pastor's turn, she noticed he adopted a soft, sympathetic voice. Almost whiny. It was out of character for him. This was how he presented his idea. Kiz discerned something in his voice that told her he was thumbing his nose at the other suggestions. She felt as if they were being railroaded and manipulated.

He instantly switched gears back into his boisterous self. He made the decision that it was going to be his idea. There was no discussion or vote. Without asking for volunteers, he started assigning work. The date and time had already been set. He had made all of the plans himself. Why had he even bothered to ask people what they would like to do?

Kiz helped with two more of the pastor's projects and noticed that attendance at the meetings was dropping dramatically. None of the projects he had chosen in advance benefited the community in any way. After he referred to the congregation as HIS audience, Kiz dropped out.

Not because she didn't want to serve or help, she did. She felt driven to serve and help the people who needed to be served and helped the most. And he and his ego wasn't one of them.

She made hats and scarves galore along with a few lap rugs thrown in. She volunteered more time at the homeless shelter. And she continued attending Church.

Until…one Sunday the music was so loud her chest was vibrating. When several requests from other Church members to turn it down were denied, she felt she'd had enough.

She prayed that the music during communion would be toned down enough so she could thank Jesus properly for what He had done. It wasn't. The worship leader sang a solo with his guitar and microphone turned up full blast. As her chest vibrated out of control, she took her cup of juice and wafer and left the sanctuary.

Kneeling in the parking lot, Kiz prayed for forgiveness if she was being judgmental. She thanked Jesus in as special a way as she could while the pavement vibrated under her.

Kiz went in for the rest of the service. How did the 70-90 crowd feel? It couldn't have been physically good for them. She didn't like the chest vibrating sensation at all when she was a lot younger and had attended a few concerts.

She particularly didn't like it at almost 60. In a Church no less. After twenty months, she decided this wasn't where she should be. The rest of them, though, (she loved all), could let the world assault them in a House of Prayer, but she couldn't stay.

Chapter 18

She didn't know what she was in for when she prayed that original prayer. Not that it mattered much. She had meant it then and she meant it now. The Light was Shining and she was beginning to see things for what they really were. And they were ugly.

Kiz had started leading a study at one of the Churches she had attended. She chose "Job" because of the lessons that needed to be learned. A few women came for a couple weeks, but that didn't last long. Of course, the world got in the way. Better, more important things to do than study the Bible. Kiz, though, was faithful to show up every week with the lesson prepared; even if no one came to share it with her.

She had become pretty well versed on the ways Satan worked. She was beginning to recognize his deception, actions and reasoning. Like when she was sweeping at a friend's house. The sweeper sucked in a cord for a laptop, ripping both ends off. She knew immediately what she had to do, but her mind was fighting it.

Maybe they wouldn't notice. You could throw it away and let them wonder what happened to it. You could put it on the living room floor and let them think the dog chewed it up. So many easy ways out; so many temptations. Was the human mind really that evil? How many Christians actually took the wrong way out? In the end, she did what was right. She told them what happened.

When her employment world began to fall apart, Satan's ways and means were obvious. There was pain and grief, friends she had made over years of serving them started to either turn on her or decide they didn't need her anymore.

She could see evil working in their lives, but they couldn't. Kiz seriously wondered if she was being attacked. As each person she considered to be a friend fell away, her sadness deepened.

She never questioned God. There seemed to be a knowing in her that her life was about to change. Which way or which direction it was going to take was a mystery, but as income dwindled, she leaned more heavily on her Savior. She was confident He had something in store for her. Kiz was sure it all had everything to do with that voice in her head telling her as a child that she was meant to do something important.

Kizzy didn't harbor any grand ideas that there was going to be an idyllic outcome. She didn't see any rose gardens in her future on earth. Maybe the thorns, but Kiz decided she would take whatever was to come and try to find God's Truth and Beauty in it.

> *"For they that are of the flesh do mind the things*
> *of the flesh,"*
> *In Romans 8:5*

The friends Kiz had just lost hurt her the most. She helped people who couldn't do it themselves. She considered herself to be just a general house cleaner. Kiz believed what the Bible said about the things of the world. We weren't to attach a label of too much importance to them. God is a jealous God; He is above all else. That was supposed to include our homes and furnishings.

Kiz had helped an elderly couple for almost five years. She absolutely was not a perfectionist, but did as good a job as she could do. Some things might occasionally be missed and other things just never crossed her mind. As her eyes were opening, the attacks began.

The elderly woman started scrutinizing everything. The traffic pattern in the old carpet was Kiz's fault because she didn't sweep good enough. Worn

S.S. Riley

away finish on the old floors was her fault because she was using the wrong cleaner.

Anything Kiz missed or didn't get up-to-snuff was pointed out in quite a mean way. If one tiny crumb was left on a counter, the woman would leave it there. Two weeks later when Kiz went back, the finger was going towards the crumb. Every time she went to the house, something miniscule wasn't good enough.

They stopped talking to her at all, except to put her down or give her a sharp answer to any question she had. These had been dear, beloved friends to her. She thought the evil one had to be the driving force in their constant criticism and growing hatred of her.

After about six months of this, Kiz was uneasy about going to their home. But they needed help. As much as she dreaded going back to find out what she had done wrong or badly, she loved them and cared deeply.

On Kiz's last day, the woman had come out of the family room in the basement. Kiz was about halfway done with the first floor. There was no hello, how are you, only a terse "if you even bothered to clean the sink in the bathroom you did a tirrible job." Then she walked away.

It was "tirrible?" Not terrible? Kizzy had burst into tears and sobs as a bedroom door slammed shut. She knew she wasn't the best, she had told them that long ago. Immaculate wasn't in her vocabulary, but she knew the sink couldn't be THAT bad. She also knew the devil must be at work here. If these dear Christian friends had come to hate her because of earthly treasures, there was only one thing she could do. She fired herself on the spot.

She sniffed and wiped her eyes as she put their things back where they belonged. Then she quietly gathered up her own stuff and left the house halfway done. She cried as she walked to her car.

Kiz didn't want to do it this way and didn't like that she had done it this way. If it wasn't going to be good enough anyhow, why bother to do it at all? She spent the rest of the day in prayer, asking forgiveness for whatever she had done to them, deep sadness and bouts of sobbing.

She didn't know what else God was going to let the evil one do in her life. But she did feel that something else was about to happen. Not meaning it would be good.

Kiz lay on her bed and pondered many things as she wiped her eyes and blew her nose. Her sadness wasn't for the loss of income and maybe not even for the loss of cherished people. But more because how easily Satan could sway solid, God fearing followers. She knew, she had been there. It wasn't hard at all, it didn't take much.

> *"for I have learned, in whatsoever state I am in,*
> *there with to be content."*
> *In Philippians 4:11*

Kiz let her mind wander over the Mystery that was the Lord. Things that were, to us, nothing more than a royal pain were glorious in His Eyes. She would try her hardest to find that Glory in her current situation. She helped at a homeless shelter. Maybe that's where she would end up. A lot of souls needed nurturing there. She could do that. Bring Glory to God out of what seemed to be despair.

For some reason a certain woman kept coming into her mind. A woman who was between jobs. She cried and carried on so. Kiz couldn't count the number of times she had heard her say, "Okay, God, I want my life back now." It had given Kiz an eerie feeling, like maybe the woman had no idea what was involved in following Christ.

Kiz hadn't tried to console the woman at the time because nothing was going to do that except a high-paying job with excellent benefits. The Lord gives and the Lord takes away. She did pray that the woman would get the job she wanted. Only Kiz could see a problem with that. Maybe the Lord had something else in mind that the woman couldn't see or wasn't interested in. Was this some kind of test?

Kiz didn't believe that people came into our lives by accident or that they left by accident. Remembering this helped calm her. She didn't want the attitude the other woman was carrying. Maybe that's why they had crossed paths. An example. She thought that some we were to teach and some were to teach us.

She smiled about all of the deceitful, irritating, angry people she had met. She decided she must appear that way to some. Oh, how many tests she had failed! She let attacks of the evil one slip from her mind as she thought about what Jesus had done and how He had saved us. No matter what else or who else would be taken out of her life, she knew it would be the Potter's Hand at work.

Chapter 19

"Train up a child in the way he should go; and when
he is old, he will not depart from it."
Proverbs 22:6

When the true meaning of this verse got through to Kiz, it cut her to the quick.
It was a mouthful waiting to be spit out. We were treating our kids like idols,
worshipping them. What would they grow up to think they were? Idols that
should be worshipped? Kiz had probably skimmed over this verse a dozen or
more times, but now it finally had meaning.

In her highly sensitized state, she saw it for what it was. Prophesy. An omen.
Solomon. The wisest man on earth. A word from the wise that only God could
let you decipher. Yes, how true it was. The child of alcoholic parents usually
ended up a drunk. Shooting up heroin or crack? Look out! Abusive parents
produced abusive children.

There was a lot of bad behavior being trained onto our children. However,
the biggest part of the population was consumed with things. Lots and lots of
things. It was clear to Kiz that as parents worshipped their idol kids they were
letting the little kiddywinks develop idols of their own. Whether the idols were
cartoon characters, musicians, styles of music, TV shows, TV stars, sports fig-
ures, sports teams, types of sports, whatever they were, it showed everywhere.

Toys, pajamas, book bags, sports equipment, clothes, shoes, hats, gloves, coats, toothbrushes, plastic dishes, you name it. They were advertising their idols. You could usually tell by looking at a child which idols they were most fond of.

The parents didn't even know they were doing it. Indulging the child's every whim. The ones who bought, bought, bought were raising kids who were going to buy, buy, buy. We had become gluttons for things. We couldn't be satisfied because we worshipped more and more things. There was always more we and our children wanted. We had to have it.

So, Kiz wondered, where did God fit into this big mess of things? When and where did Jesus come in? Sunday mornings? Probably nowhere. Our quest for things was all consuming. It was all so cute, so pretty, so sparkly, so cool, so enticing. And we were teaching it to our kids. What was going to happen when you couldn't buy ANYTHING without the mark of the beast? Maybe we should start teaching some restraint.

> *"Chasten thy son while there is hope, and let*
> *not thy soul spare for his crying."*
> *Proverbs 19:18*

> *"Withhold not correction from the child: for if thou beatest him*
> *with a rod, he shall not die. Thou shalt beat him with a*
> *rod, and shalt deliver his soul from hell."*
> *Proverbs 12:13,14*

Yeah. Like this was ever going to happen. Everyone screamed child abuse. It was too important to most parents that their kids liked them. Kiz had seen so many children that needed a good spanking, it wasn't even funny.

If parents wouldn't make their kids obey them in even the simplest things, how in the world were the children ever to be able to obey an even stricter Parent, Father God Almighty?

Kiz wasn't in favor of brutal beatings and cruel punishment in any way. She didn't think the Bible was either. It wasn't all or nothing, there had to be a happy medium.

No matter what the kids did, it was okay. They would grow out of it or they were too young to control their anger. Any excuse for the acceptance of their behavior was better than taking control of the problem. NOT! Kiz really didn't hold out much hope for their futures. Or their souls. They weren't being taught any respect for anything. As long as more stuff would shut them up for awhile, that's what they got.

Over and over again a poem she had read as a child kept coming into her head. It was several months before the reason started becoming clear. Odd though, she didn't remember memorizing it, but the words were in her head.

Little Orphant Annie

By James Whitcomb Riley (1849-1916)

(Used by permission of the laws governing public domain. All credit and appreciation applied to the author.)

"Little orphant Annie's come to our house to stay,
An' wash the cups and saucers up, an' brush the crumbs away.
An' shoo the chickens off the porch, an' dust the hearth, an' sweep.
An' make the fire, an' bake the bread, an' earn her board-an-keep;
An' all us other children, when the supper things is done,
We set around the kitchen fire an' has the mostest fun
A-list'nin' to the witch-tales 'at Annie tells about,
An' the gobble-uns 'at gits you
Ef You Don't Watch Out!"

Since the Lord had been teaching her to think, to analyze everything that touched her life, Kiz treated this no differently. It had been given to her for a reason, so she paid close attention.

Even though Annie was an orphan, it sounded as if she had been taught some valuable lessons. She was industrious and had a lot of talent. Bread wasn't easy to make, neither was a fire. She kept busy at mundane things, as we all should.

What were the other children doing while Annie was being good and working? Probably not much. They were probably spoiled brats. Whenever Kiz had a parent lovingly tell her their kids were spoiled, the word "ruined" crossed her mind. More than likely they were. Ruined for anything worthwhile for the Lord.

Annie sounded to Kizzy like Ruth. But who would know who Ruth was or anything about her story?

"Wunst they was a little boy wouldn't say his prayers,
An' when he went to bed at night, away up stairs,
His mammy heerd him holler, an' his daddy heerd him bawl,
An' when they turn't the kivvers down, he wuzn't there at all!
An' they seeked him in the rafter room an' cubby hole, an' press,
An' they seeked him up the chimbly-flue, an' everywhere I guess;
But all they ever found was his pants an' round about:
An' the gobble-uns'll git you,
Ef You Don't Watch Out!

An' one time a little girl 'ud allus laugh and grin,
An' make fun of ever'one, an' all her blood-an' kin;
An' wunst when they was "company" an 'ole folks was there,
She mocked 'em an' shocked 'em, an' said she didn't care!
An' thist as she kicked her heels, an' turn't to run an' hide,
They wuz two great big Black Things a-standin' by her side,
An' they snatched her through the ceilin' 'fore she knowed what
She's about!
An' the gobble-uns'll git you
Ef You Don't Watch Out!

Is this what Annie's wise little mind saw as she watched the other children? The mention of prayers gave the indication that there was some Biblical teaching in her background. Was Annie, in her childlike state trying to warn them about what was going to happen to their souls? She obviously cared or she wouldn't have told them.

S.S. Riley

Kizzy was sure this state of unruly obliviousness occurred in nearly every child. How could they learn what they weren't being taught? Lack of discipline was one of the roads to hell. God knew it, that's why He constantly disciplined us.

What was with these stupid time-outs that were so popular nowadays anyhow? Kiz hated them. If the only consequence of bad behavior was sitting in a chair for five minutes, it wasn't much of a deterrent. An angry child sitting in a chair. Perfect opportunity for the evil one to plant more seeds of unrest and obnoxiousness. Kiz was stumped at the lack of wisdom or effectiveness in this practice.

Heaven forbid we even come close to scaring our perfect little angels. They had to be coddled and kept on the high end of the ego trip. What would telling them, if they didn't straighten up they were going to burn in hell forever and ever, do to them? Was it better to just withhold the information? Yes, that was love, it was the best thing to do. Literally. Keep them in the dark. Satan's dark.

"An' little orphan Annie says, when the blaze is blue,
An' the lamp-wick sputters, an' the wind goes woo-oo!
An' you hear the crickets quit, an' the moon is gray,
An' lightnin' bugs in dew is all squenched away,
You better mind yer parents, an' yer teachers fond an' dear,
An' churish them 'at loves you, an' dry the orphan's tear,
An' he'p the poor an' needy ones 'at clusters all about,
Er the gobble- uns'll git you
Ef You Don't Watch Out!"

No mention of Jesus and what He had done, but the wisdom of the child was poignant. Do the good works we were saved to do. People needed to wake up and quit playing games with their children's souls. This was serious stuff.

"His children are far from safety…"
In Job 5:4

"For when they shall say, Peace and safety; then
sudden destruction cometh upon them…and they
shall not escape."
In 1 Thessalonians 5:3

Kiz wasn't sure if the Lord was done giving her the little bit of understanding she had so solemnly prayed for, so she kept her receptors open, just in case. She prayed a lot, but not on her knees as much as she should. She stuck to changes that had been made in her life and wondered how she could get the information to others in a congenial way.

As days passed, Kiz began to notice a copy-size paper stuck to a phone pole on one of the main roads she traveled. Brain damage was all she could read from her car. Finally, after seeing it for a couple weeks, the Lord laid it on her heart to check it out. She drove to the spot, parked on a side street and walked to the sign, pen in hand.

"Vaccines cause brain damage" it said. There was a website listed so she wrote it down. www.vaccinetruth.org. Kiz was completely computer illiterate and planned to stay that way. So she went to the library and asked for help.

Once on the website, she found many things to her complete horror. Abortions were forced on cows, pigs and rhesus monkeys. Certain tissues were used in children's shots and what was left of the carcasses was sold to the food industry. The poor helpless creatures were creamed and added to food. They were listed on ingredient labels as "hydrolyzed animal protein."

Kizzy's eyes began to burn, but she brushed the tears away. God had bestowed mothering instincts into most creatures He created. These animals that were having abortions forced on them had to be suffering untold myriad pain. Human DNA from aborted fetuses was used. There were elements that caused cancer, blindness, and sterility, just to name a few.

How about shooting your newborn up with some antifreeze? Want your kid to have seizures? Go for it. Neurological disorders? Piece of cake. No problem. Put a little aluminum and mercury into the mix. See what happens. Immune system damage? Yep. Add a little formaldehyde there, won't you? Please? It causes cancer you know. How about the same glue that's used to hold labels on glass bottles? A little casein never hurt anybody. Or did it? A little MSG to eat away at the retina. Plus, it activates and stimulates nerves so much that they go crazy and die.

Mercury. Hmm...it was banned from contact solution and animal vaccines because it is so dangerous. So why are we still injecting it into our helpless bundles of joy? Mercury damages the brain and kidneys and causes birth defects. Mercury has been proven to increase autism cases through the environment. Why are we deliberately putting it into our children?

Kiz had barely stuck her toe in the water and was petrified. She logged off of the computer and stumbled to her car. We were also worshipping the poisoning of our offspring and were training them to do it to theirs. Evil, pure and simple. The human race had put themselves in serous trouble. Demanding the deliberate poisoning of their children.

"And He knoweth them that trust in Him."
In Nahum 1:7

"It is better to trust in the Lord than to put confidence
in man."
Psalm 118:8

Kiz was as guilty as the rest. She always claimed she trusted God, but her heart had been far from Him. Was it fear and deception that caused us to rely on such evil things? Anyone that said they trusted God wasn't being completely honest. No one she knew did. They trusted more in the world and the things it had to offer. Our children were suffering because of it. We were all suffering and as far as Kiz could see, we deserved it. We were bringing it on ourselves.

As time wore on, she realized she had been changed: sadder, depressed again, not wanting to be around to watch it anymore. She never got over what she had learned in just those few minutes on www.vaccinetruth:org. It hit her like a Mack truck. It put her down. She didn't think she would ever recover. We were following the beast, not the Lord, and we were headed for slaughter. People must be told.

Chapter 20

"For My yoke is easy, and My burden is light."
Matthew 11:30

Kiz must not have made it there yet because it sure didn't feel that way. Again, she found it was all she could do to maintain her responsibilities. She slept. And slept some more. But she kept waking up and the world was still there.

She prayed over and over again for the joy and peace of soul that Jesus had promised. Could personal happiness be attained on this planet? Her brain kept telling her no, but something deep inside was saying yes.

Whenever the thought started to enter her mind that maybe she shouldn't have requested understanding, she shoved it away. It was God's Will or this wouldn't be happening. Did those thoughts keep coming back because Satan was niggling at her? Or because she was human?

It didn't matter. Whatever it was, she made it go away. Yes, she did want to know the truth. After many years of living for herself and letting evil have it's way with her, she truly wanted to live a life that was pleasing to God. Kiz mustered her strength and cleared her mind. On her knees she told her King that, if there was more, she was ready.

As was seemingly the case lately, bits and pieces of one subject would come to her with some truth about it. Then information about something else would enter her mind with startling implications. This is what was happening now. She was having a hard time categorizing and sorting out what was being delivered to her. Maybe she was trying, thinking too hard.

She was absolutely sure that the Lord had it all figured out. She just needed to relax and wait. Knowing there was so much more to materialism than she had been given so far, she settled in to embark on new territory of which she had been ignorant. Of all the other subjects invading her brain, that one, material worship, seemed to be the most prominent.

Kiz opened her mind to the Spirit and waited while thoughts, ideas and information filtered in. Two versus came to the forefront of her mind.

"The Lord knoweth how to deliver the Godly out of temptations, and to reserve the unjust unto the day of judgment to be punished: But chiefly them that walk after the flesh in the lust of uncleanness, and despise government. Presumptuous are they, self willed, they are not afraid to speak evil of dignities."
2 Peter 2:9,10

"Likewise also these filthy dreamers defile the flesh, despise dominion, and speak evil of dignities."
In Jude verse 8

These verses that were pointed out stopped Kiz dead in her tracks. Even things she wasn't aware she was feeling, thinking or saying. The government was put in place by Almighty God.

Kiz looked and looked but couldn't find the passage she was thinking of. She knew she would get it wrong if she didn't go directly to the Bible for it. Something about the law being for evil people and if you were righteous, what did you have to fear from government? Not finding it didn't throw up a roadblock for her. She would get there eventually.

The government was for the good of the people, depending on their behavior. God could use it for reward or punishment, as He saw fit. Kiz got on her knees and asked for advice on what she needed to change within her to be more in line with God's Will towards our leaders. What she got was a cold chill. It had felt to her for a long time that a government of the people, by the people and for the people was anything but. She remembered what happened when the ancients demanded a king.

As she thought about it seriously, a black cloud formed over her. People, people, people. Where was God in all of this? On our currency and coins? Maybe that was the biggest downfall of all.

"Because the foolishness of God is wiser than men..."
In 1 Corinthians 1:25

"For the wisdom of this world is foolishness with God."
In 1 Corinthians 3:19

Yes, men were flighty. They changed their minds and dwelt on things that were not of God. She knew, she was the same way. A foolish person. She smiled. Everyone had their own agenda. THEY knew what was best.

While she made changes in her attitude towards a government of mere men, she stopped her mouth about what was going on. It still didn't change the fact that it was being laid on her heart to examine man's policies more closely. And the implications of where those policies were leading us.

"only if thou carefully hearken unto the Voice of the Lord thy
God, to observe to do all these Commandments which I
Command thee this day. For the Lord thy God blesseth thee,
as He promised thee: and thou shalt lend unto many nations,
but thou shalt not borrow; and thou shalt reign over many
nations, but they shalt not reign over thee."
Deuteronomy 15:5,6

Yes, this was a promise to God's people. And she got the "but if." Only if. There was something here Kiz couldn't figure out. It would take prayer and meditation if she was allowed to know the answer at all. Was it even any of her business to know the answer? What did it matter? What difference would it make?

If all men were created equal, why did God only choose a very small group to be His people? Why not everyone? Why did the Bible state that God loved Jacob but Esau He hated? Why were souls predestinated to one of two places before they were ever born? Questions mounted again.

It seemed to her now that Jesus had been sacrificed for all of us that these promises would apply to all. But what nation was seriously hearkening carefully to the Voice of God? None of them. It sounded that, if we honestly did, we would be blessed beyond our wildest imaginings. But all she could see was that "In God We Trust" was being flushed down the toilet piece by piece, a little more each day.

So we were not listening to the Voice of God. We were doing whatever we wanted to do. The Bible was full of "but if you don't's," and we weren't, so that put us where? On the borrowing end? Not on the lending end? If we were led to believe we were actually doing "good," the sin of owing would seem okay. Wouldn't it? But it wasn't okay. She remembered that the evil one twisted evil to make it look good.

So we were borrowing lots and lots of money. Trillions upon trillions. We were up to our eyeballs in debt because of it and there was no way it could ever be repaid.

We were barely able to make the interest payment. Nothing was coming off the principal. Still, we continued to borrow. Unwise? Bad business? Not for China. If Kiz didn't know better, she would have to believe that the Lord was abundantly blessing a nation that didn't confess to believe in Him.

It happened before in the Bible and it led to bad news for those that claimed to trust and believe. God is in control. He is All-powerful, All-mighty and All-knowing. Her fears subsided.

What was the need for all this money? Where was it all going? Huge, gigantic amounts of money. When the answer came, she wasn't a bit surprised.

S.S. Riley

For a country that claimed to be a God-loving, God-fearing group of people, we were headed in the opposite direction. Far, far away from where we should be. All of this money was desperately needed to support sin. Evil, filthy, ungodly, sinful behavior.

> *"a rich man shall hardly enter into the Kingdom of Heaven.*
> *And again I say unto you, It is easier for a camel*
> *to go through the eye of a needle, than for a rich man to enter*
> *into the Kingdom of God."*
> *In Matthew 19:23,24*

> *"And they lay wait for their own blood; they lurk privily for their*
> *own lives. So are the ways of every one that is greedy of gain;"*
> *In Proverbs 1:18,19*

> *"For I know your manifold transgressions and your*
> *mighty sins: they afflict the just, they take a bribe."*
> *In Amos 5:12*

It had been quite awhile since she'd had her whole cable package turned off, but Kiz clearly remembered seeing a story on the news about the fastest growing area of new multi-millionaires in the country. All clumped tightly in the area of Virginia, right around Washington D.C. Not unusual news, rather quite expected. The man reporting the story wore an amused look on his face.

She also recently heard that there were more lobbyists on Capitol Hill than there were politicians. She understood a lobbyist's job was to 'convince' those politicians to back big business interests. She also understood that they did this with big sums of money. Were threats involved? Probably.

It seemed kind of useless to her because from what she had heard, big business had more power than the politicians and pretty much ran the country. They got what they wanted regardless of who they hurt or how badly they hurt them.

Was any of this vast ocean of borrowed money going into the pockets of these newly made millionaire politicians? Or did their money all come from big business? Or both? How much of the borrowed money was going to big business?

Something wasn't right. Government employees were raking in far more than their employers and giving themselves rights and perks that were denied to said employers. The American public.

Unholy, shifty practices were the norm. They were accepted and expected. It was all part of the game. It occurred to Kiz that the general population was as guilty as those caught up in the bribery. Instead of saying no, we won't have it any longer and voting them out of office, we were turning a blind eye on it as we were on every other wrong we encountered.

> *"And a certain man lame from his mother's womb was carried,*
> *whom they laid daily at the gate of the temple which is*
> *called Beautiful, to ask alms of them that entered*
> *the temple."*
> *Acts 3:2*

Kiz was dumbfounded by some of the things she saw. She asked the Lord to forgive her hard-heartedness and tell her what to think about some of the things she was witnessing. Even a lame man chose to work, no matter how degrading it must have been. He was contributing something for his family, doing something productive with his time.

Things began to bother her. Greatly. Not really in a judgmental way, she didn't think, but maybe she was wrong. Truthfully, she just didn't understand.

Like the elderly lady in the real fur, ankle length coat and expensive clothes in front of her in the grocery line. Paying with food stamps. When Kiz left the store she saw the woman putting the last of her bags into the trunk of a brand new white Cadillac. It still had thirty-day tags on it.

And the twenty-something guy with handicapped plates on his Hummer. He jumped out laughing and beating his chest. He appeared to her to be able to carry a refrigerator up the steps by himself with no trouble at all. He also bought food with food stamps.

And the white car with county plates that was parked crossway on the three handicapped spaces. There was a wheelchair parking pass hanging from the rearview mirror. She saw no one she could categorize as handicapped milling around in the store.

And the woman in nurse's garb with a hospital name tag on her shirt, using food stamps and bragging that she only wore Black Hills gold. She was dripping with it.

And the woman who complained that WIC gave her too much milk. Instead of just getting what she needed, she got it all and threw it away.

Kiz knew a great many people were taking advantage of a system that was completely broken. People were taking as much as they could get for free. The problem was, nothing was free. Someone somewhere was paying for all of this needless excess. And paying dearly.

The answer Kiz got to her prayers actually made her feel sorry for them. They had their reward. They got what was important to them. After this, it bothered her in a completely different way.

> *"her candle goeth not out by night."*
> *In Proverbs 31:18*

> *"as when the bright shining of a candle doth give thee light."*
> *In Luke 11:36*

So, how did all this come about? This huge demand for so much energy? We were gluttons for it. She never thought there could be greed and lust for this kind of power, but there it was. When all we needed really was enough light to see by, where did the rest fit in? Oh, yes, destruction of the world and big business. Lots of money there! With the onset of her fruitcake state she wasn't sure that all of these things she was beginning to see were the truth. But government had it's hand in energy big time.

Satan was busy day and night inflicting his deception on the people. Kiz knew she was no exception. Why did we need so much energy from the world while neglecting our own power? Because the world kept telling us we needed it? She knew she was confused but why was it making so much sense?

And men were scorched with great heat…"
In Revelation 16:9

Hmm…good old global warming? As Kiz studied the book of Revelation over and over, she realized the prophecies were coming true. Scientists had proven that burning fossil fuels was the main cause. As time progressed, she noticed that not once did anyone suggest we just stop using so much and cut way back. The focus was on getting more so we could use more. Those all-important rules and regulations just meant more money in the pockets of the bigwigs.

The money was too big. The demand was too high. Energy was precious. It was a dangerous game. A game of the world. A game we were all going to lose in the end.

If God was content with the way things were progressing, the book of Revelation would never have been written. But He wasn't and the key word here was "progress."

Progress was the reason that government policies had to be put in place. Use as much as you want, but we're going to make you pay dearly. We're going to put stronger restrictions on all fuels and demand higher and higher monetary penalties. It's always about money. They didn't care about the environment.

We'll give billions of borrowed dollars to countries like Peru for offshore drilling, but it's too dangerous to do it here. Our shores are deathbeds already. We'll just expand it all around the rest of the globe. Make sure all of our shores are coated with deadly toxins.

The only way anyone in a position of power had proposed any reduction in the use of fossil fuels was to expand nuclear energy. That was just as bad or even worse. The reactors leaked and vast amounts of water became unusable. The waste was buried in the ground just waiting for a bomb to be dropped on it. And why were the biggest majority of them built on fault lines where earthquakes could easily tumble them?

Hadn't we learned anything from past experience? It was unsafe and proven to pollute huge areas when it malfunctioned. Hey…we could even build small

S.S. Riley

reactors in every town and village to supply their ever-growing demand for energy. Make sure the danger is everywhere. Kiz knew for a fact that a diabolical plan was brewing.

> *"Except the Lord build the house, they labour in*
> *vain that build it…"*
> In Psalm 127:1

Was it the Lord that was building our house? Our government? Was His Hand in it? Kiz had read, but couldn't remember where, that the Holiness of God prevented Him from even looking upon sin. That's why the Blood of Christ washed us continually. So we could have fellowship with the Creator. Still, Kiz found herself wondering if He had left our government to its own devices.

The government was more than willing to give us all the energy we demanded, but it came at a stiff cost. The price we had to pay would only increase. It wasn't about looking out for the people. It was looking out for itself.

Kiz could see that she was part of a nation full of Christians who were flailing around madly in the darkness. No amount of energy provided was going to fix that problem. We only had one direction… GO! There seemed to be no firm foundation that we were building on.

We were seeking fulfillment outside the Word of God. We were insatiably partaking of what the world had to offer. It wasn't filling the empty void inside us, so we sought more…and more…and more.

It wasn't going to stop. It would never stop. Until God stopped it. In our blindness we are driven by greed and lust. We wanted it, we wanted it bad and we wanted it now. Stuff, money, prestige, action, relief from boredom, escaping our thoughts, enlarging our kid's interests and experiences of the world and it all took some sort of energy.

There is no stillness or peace in us. We wished for it and prayed for it, but it eluded us. By our own consumption of more and more energy we would never find it. We, God's people, were letting the world run us to a smoking, frazzled mess of humanity, like the smoldering, lifeless carcass of a burned out vehicle.

That's what our consumption of energy was beginning to look like to Kiz. How much longer until our whole, entire planet would take on that image? Would God let it go that far? It felt to her like it was fast approaching.

Until we stopped using so much energy and forking over so much cash to use it, the government would spare no expense to make sure we got it. When were we going to stop and count the real costs?

"The greater light to rule the day, and the lesser light
to rule the night:"
In Genesis 1:16

As Kiz prayed, pondered and meditated on this growing, poisonous, destructive problem, the answer for her became obvious. She extricated herself and her home from every power-sucking device that was not necessary for survival. Her home became cold and dark in the winter, bright and hot during the summer. Comfort was thrown out the window.

She kept one electric alarm clock in her bedroom. There was only ever one light bulb on at a time, if and when she needed one. And that wasn't always. She kept the stove, refrigerator, washer and dryer. The rest went away. She found she liked to cook over a fire outside and mainly used a clothesline.

When Kiz called to cancel her cable package and everything that went with it, a cold chill went through her when she found she had to argue with the young man she was dealing with. He was appalled and disgusted that she would even consider withdrawing herself from such a wonderful service.

He even claimed she would no longer be able to get "the word." That clinched it. The Word to her was Something Else entirely. All Else. She didn't want the world's words anymore.

It was her turn to be appalled and disgusted when she received seventeen calls within three days of cancellation. Did she have any idea what she was missing? There were offers of cut-rate service, special rates, deals, arguments, some even vaguely sounding like threats. She stuck to her guns.

S.S. Riley

Everything could continue to go on around her. She couldn't solve the world's energy problems, but she didn't have to be part of the problem herself.

Kiz didn't even want her cell phone, but needed it for what little work she had left. Otherwise she would have gotten rid of that, too. She really didn't even want a car anymore, but the world made it necessary for survival. She limited her gas consumption to an as-needed basis. She did all of her errands only when she had to go out for work or volunteer activities.

Her gadding about town had ceased. Long rides in the country were a thing of the past. Vacations and holidays were spent at home. No more going out to eat. She curbed every thought she had to get in her car and go.

Mostly she stayed home and kept busy. It surprised her after the TV was gone that she didn't have time to get everything done she wanted to do. What was getting done before? When she was parked on the couch watching TV most of the day? She smiled. Not much.

Maybe her greatly lowered energy appetite was becoming a problem for other people. A man from the electric company appeared on her porch one day. He requested an examination of her meter. Requested wasn't exactly the right word. He demanded one. He checked it to make sure it was working properly and hadn't been tampered with. She found out she was being policed in the matter. Everything checked out fine and the man walked away scratching his head. Maybe she WAS doing something right for a change.

It reminded Kiz of a bumper sticker or sign she had read somewhere. "Be the change you want to see in the world." The one change she wanted most to see was Christians getting over themselves, taking a good look at how far away they really were from Jesus and taking deliberate steps to draw nearer to their Lord. When the hammer came down, it was the only thing that was going to save us.

"We are unprofitable servants: we have done that which
was our duty to do."
In Luke 17:10

*"Doth he thank that servant because he did the things that
were commanded him? I trow not."*
In Luke 17:9

"and be content with your wages."
In Luke 3:14

This was all something Kiz was agreeing with more every day. Do your job and get paid for it. Period. End of story. But man in his pitiful wisdom wouldn't stop at that. Particularly government and big business. We weren't even supposed to be thanked for doing our job. Just get wages. Wages set by the person you did the job for. Not by the government. But things had grown out of control, hadn't they? Now we were all in a really big financial mess because we wouldn't listen to the Wisdom of Creator God.

We weren't planning our future according to the promises of God, we were planning them according to the promises of the world. And things weren't going so well. Just take a good hard look at the postal service. That should be an example of what not to do, but it didn't deter anything. We constantly added more perks and promises. More and more people every day were coming into empty promises.

We were not trusting God and living the simple lives the Bible tells us to live. If we were, things like this would not be happening. Kiz didn't hear anyone saying, "No, keep it. The Lord promised to take care of those who believe in Him. And I do."

Even Christians were screaming gimme, gimme, gimme. I need, I need, I need. How many were bypassing the miracles that the Creator and Owner of All would do in our lives if we weren't so self dependant. How many didn't really believe? Oh, so many.

We were going to pay dearly in the end for our greed and unbelief. Kiz could feel it in her bones.

"if any would not work, neither should he eat."
In 2 Thessalonians 3:10

Nowhere was the reward for sinful behavior more evident to her than in the welfare system. Who thought of this anyway? Kizzy had a pretty good idea. The evil one. Sin and get rewarded richly for it. He knew what he was doing and he was very good at doing it. He did it like it was his job.

Kiz wondered if he was getting paid or thanked for doing it. She already knew what HIS retirement package looked like. He dreams up more and more enticing, ungodly plans, luring people in and it was working perfectly.

~II~

"Therefore shall a man leave his father and his mother,
and shall cleave unto his wife; and they shall be one flesh."
Genesis 2:24

"yet is she thy companion, and the wife of thy covenant. And
did he not make one?...And wherefore one? That he might
seek a Godly seed..."
In Malachi 2:14,15

God made man and wife one flesh so he would have Godly seed. Godly seed produced Godly children. Kiz pondered this.

"Flee fornication."
In 1 Corinthians 6:18

"Know ye not that the unrighteous shall not inherit the
Kingdom of God? Be not deceived; neither fornicators...
shall inherit The Kingdom of God."
In 1 Corinthians 6:19,10

"Flee also youthful lusts..."
In 2 Timothy 2:22

What did "flee" mean? Kiz was of a mind it meant to get away from as fast as you could because of danger. And what was fornication? Sexual intercourse between unmarried persons.

Are Christians not the bride of Christ? Did not Jesus say the only grounds for divorce was fornication? Would He divorce us for that very reason?

But fornication is what welfare requires. We will fully support mothers with children born out of wedlock. That sounded sinister to her. That kind of help wasn't offered to married couples. If you were on welfare and got married, all help would cease immediately.

Sin was being promoted and encouraged. It paid well. The more children you had out of wedlock, the more the government gave you. This reward system was so profitable that it was being perpetuated from generation to generation.

Kiz once heard that welfare paid $40.00 an hour for a 40 hour workweek. Your average Joe didn't even come close to that kind of paycheck. Of course, it was vehemently denied and the amount was set at $14.00 an hour for a 40 hour workweek. Still, not many she knew made even that much on their jobs.

She had a hard time believing the lowered total. Even that amount was shocking. When you threw in everything: all of those vouchers, housing, utilities, food stamps, WIC, medical care, child care, debit cards, etc. she believed it could be more than $40.00 per hour. But what did she know?

Considering we were a nation enamored with stuff and ridiculous amounts of things we deemed necessary, it didn't appear that anyone was going to give it up to live a Godly life. We demanded more every day.

For her, welfare took on the visage of an evil trap. It was impossible to get out of welfare in today's world and the only way to stay in it was to keep having more illegitimate kids. Kiz was seeing it as a fast track to hell.

Another immoral and evil twist rode in on welfare's coattails. Kiz had lived in a very poor and rundown part of the city for ten years. She had witnessed it firsthand in her neighborhood on a daily basis. Not just occasionally, but always. It was a way of life, deeply ingrained in not just this particular group of people, but nationwide.

"So God created man in His Own Image, in the Image
of God created He him;"
In Genesis 1:27

Whether women like it or not, men are above women. It is God's plan and design. Man is to be the head, the ruler of the family. This did not sit well with many. Particularly the evil one. In his pursuit of destroying man, Satan is hell-bent on corrupting, polluting, maiming and belittling him in every way possible.

It was the man's responsibility to provide for his family. Welfare became the perfect way to take this responsibility away. If an illegitimate child was claimed by the father, he was smacked with a ridiculous amount of child support. This wouldn't do because it was counter-productive to how much income could be derived from the state.

Nine times out of ten, the father or another man lived with the woman and children the system was supporting. His roles as provider and protector were being usurped by greed and law. If it was known that a male was living in the home, well…The provider had become a parasite. Men were becoming worthless in their God-given role. They were pushed away and downgraded.

Welfare was reducing the leader to the least. God's greatest creation, man, was being stripped of everything that made him a real man. All responsibility was taken away and was replaced by nothing except idleness, a lostness.

The void left by time that should have been filled with being responsible was leading to self destructive and criminal behavior. Kiz saw it everywhere around her. Grown men and teenage boys gathered on porches smoking weed and crack and drinking all day. A lawn was mowed once in a while, but there wasn't much else productive going on. It was quiet during daylight hours, but after dark all hell broke loose.

Fights, prostitution, gun shots, breaking into and stealing cars, rapes, breaking and entering, robberies, murders, stealing anything that wasn't bolted down or locked up. The police blotter had grown to more than a full page in the newspaper. Kiz had seen dead, murdered bodies lying in the streets and sitting in cars.

And speaking of cars, she had never seen so many expensive ones in her life. How could men who didn't work drive a BMW, a Lexus or an Escalade, Hummer, Tahoe, Land Rover, Jaguar or Durango. Mostly huge gas guzzlers. She didn't think welfare paid THAT much and suspected drug manufacturing and sales had a little to do with it. But she wasn't about to go knocking on doors and asking. Eventually many of the men and boys ended up dead or in prison. Some, she was sure, were involved in the string of revenge killings.

Yep, "Train your child up in the way he is to go and he will not depart from it." Welfare legacy, live on!

~II~

On top of the useless, lost feelings these men must harbor, there was possibly brain damage from the vaccinations that were forced on us by the powers that be. They screamed "don't give aspirin to a child" because it causes encephalitis, a swelling and inflamation of the covering of the brain which can cause brain damage.

But some immunizations did the very same thing. A nurse she had met at Church told her this was part of how they worked. We were purposely being damaged and once the damage was done it couldn't be undone. It was a proven fact that boys were many times more susceptible to this serious brain damage than girls. More boys were being treated for autism than girls. A lot of times there was no treatment at all. It is considered to be just the way a person is. With impaired thinking, learning disabilities and addictions on top of everything else, men were reduced even further. Satan's work was never done.

Was there any kind of education going on about any of these issues? Of course not. There was no profitability in good stuff. What profit was there in clean, healthy, wholesome bodies? None. There was profit in treating STD's, gunshot wounds and drug overdoses.

What the people really needed was their Savior, but He was the farthest thing from their minds. Until they got themselves into really serious trouble.

"And thy teachers have transgressed against Me…"
In Isaiah 43:27

No one was going to listen to what Kiz believed to be the truth. All of this stuff was "good." It was all solution to some of the problems of the world. Should Kiz even bother to try to explain where all of this was taking us?

According to the Bible, the young are to be taught by the elders. That wasn't happening any time soon. There was no respect for elders anymore. We were so warped and misled by Satan and his world that we weren't interested in advice or wisdom from anyone. Even the elders seemed to be absorbed into the world and seeking after their own way. Any wisdom anyone had was being buried under stuff.

Who wanted to hear old, ugly, wrinkled up dinosaurs talk anyway. They were stuck in the dark ages. Culture had shown us the glory of young and beautiful. Culture had taught us to follow our dreams, do our own thing no matter what. No matter how stupid or destructive it was. Wisdom was a thing of the past. The world had too much to offer.

> *"He that hath an ear, let him hear..."*
> *Several places in the Bible*

It slowly drifted into Kiz's mind that the events in the Book of Revelation wouldn't involve morphing into some weird little world where things would be different somehow. It would still be the world we lived in, the same world we saw and moved around in every day.

Most of the people she tried to talk to about it pulled back in revulsion. They didn't read the Bible because it was too scary. They refused to talk about it for the same reason. Little did they know it was creeping up on them. They couldn't hide forever.

So Kiz had no one to talk to except the Lord since she had fired herself from the home of the only older man who talked to her of Biblical things. Not that it was bad, the Lord was always there to listen. The weakening of our military through financial cuts. rumors of underground armies to "control" the population in the event of civil war or unrest.

Over taxing of people who worked to support rampant, blatant, outright sinful behavior. Borrowing huge amounts of money, backing big business that was destroying the environment, lives and property. She wanted to think it was the fault of government, but knew better. God was allowing it to happen because of idol worship and disobedience. There was no one to blame but ourselves.

The last five years had brought us closer to the "need" for a one-world government than we ever were before. We had been put in a position where we could be easily overpowered. We were sold to a foreign country and it was only a matter of time before they would come calling to collect on that bill of sale.

We were purposely being brought to the brink of collapse and very few were paying any attention. Was it God's Plan? We were merrily dancing along after the pied piper called the world. It felt to Kiz that we had been put on the fast track to the end of the world as we know it.

Mankind was going to be wiped off the map.

Did the people who were doing this understand the results of their actions? Would they wake up one day like Judas Iscariot, realize what they had done and hang themselves? Their descendants would be caught up in this mess, too. Or didn't they care?

~II~

Kiz had her first hearty laugh in a long, long time. She had chosen to concentrate on materialism so what had happened? All of this other stuff came pouring out instead. Was God trying to show her she was not in control of her insanity? Was Satan trying to overwhelm her so she couldn't put the pieces together? Was there actually so much wrong in this broken world that it couldn't be put back together? Was she even supposed to be trying?

She decided she needed a long nap.

Chapter 21

"For the gifts and calling of God are without repentance."
Romans 11:29

*"Now there are diversities of gifts…For to one is given by
the Spirit the Word of Wisdom, to another the Word of
Knowledge…To another faith…to another the gift of healing…
to another the working of miracles; to another prophecy;
to another the discerning of Spirits; to another divers
kinds of tongues; to another the interpretation of tongues; But all
of these worketh that One and Self same Spirit…"*
In 1 Corinthians 12:4-11

Kiz finally felt herself being backtracked. Back to stuff, materialism, worship of things, and lots of them to be sure. When she looked at the Fruit of the Spirit and gifts from the Spirit, she decided that's where her loyalties should lie. Did anyone ever really bother to look at or for the gifts we had been given? Gifts that were to be used to Glorify God? She was sure a very few people did, but as a rule, she didn't think so.

She started examining herself and praying for the Lord to make her gifts evident and show her how He wanted them to be used. She hadn't done that before and as the spotlight was shone on her habits she cringed. There was a lot to be cleared away before those fruits could ripen.

She hadn't been using much of anything for the Lord. It had mostly been for her benefit. It was becoming clear to her that mankind was worshipping self above God. Self above all else. What we consumed proved it. We worshipped everything, from beneath the earth to beyond the stars. There was nothing that wasn't being idolized somewhere by someone. We weren't giving much of anything to God, we were giving to ourselves. Some people worshipped way more stuff than other folks, but we were all guilty.

Kiz had already gone over her body from head to toe and gotten rid of all the deception there. She slimmed down her food intake. She had gotten rid of comforts and conveniences. She had cut her utility bills by more than two-thirds. Now it was time to look elsewhere.

> *"In like manner also, that women adorn themselves in*
> *modest apparel, with shamefacedness and sobriety,*
> *not with braided hair, or gold, or pearls, or costly array; But*
> *(which becometh women professing Godliness) with good works."*
> 1 Timothy 2:9,10

Kiz was relieved that, as a rule, she had never really been consumed about her appearance. But there had been times… She decided to turn to her clothing. Anything that was expensive or lacy or lowcut or too short or too tight or too showy went into a pile. There seemed to be quite a bit. Had she been more vain than she thought?

She knew if a man looked at a woman with lust in his eyes, he had already committed adultery with her. That should have been a warning to women who said they were Christians, but it didn't seem to matter to them. We should have been more concerned with the condition of our brother's souls than we were about our appearance. But, since we were worshipping self and drawing attention to our best attributes, it didn't work that way. We didn't care. As long as we looked good in the world's eyes. But how did God see us?

Kiz had, at times, found herself embarrassed at Church. Not because of herself, but because of other people. Cleavage everywhere, form fitting expensively tailored dresses. Short, very short. Kiz was sure she saw more deep cleavage at Church than she ever did back in her bar days.

There was a pastor and his wife who let their teenage daughters wear skirts so short their underwear showed when they walked. Some of the women looked and smelled to Kiz like nothing more than expensive hookers with their patterned hose and stilletto heels. And young girls, too. No shame. There wasn't any decency. It was all a show and they were determined to be the stars.

The outward appearance was a sign of what was in the heart. She could see where hearts really were. Aggrandizing self, not pleasing God. Gifts of the Spirit had nothing to do with how we dressed or what we looked like. Spiritual gifts were being ignored and physical gifts were being flaunted.

For some reason she began to feel angry. She went through her clothes again and discarded anything that showed an image, was decorated in a flashy way or could be considered a "pop of color." The pile grew.

The focus was supposed to be on the One True God, the Son and the Spirit. Not on her. She prayed for the Lord to show her everything she shouldn't do to worship self. It was done. It was over. She was supposed to be a servant, not the one being served.

Out went purses and bags, fancy shoes and those worthless dress boots that were for show and didn't even begin to keep your feet warm. Panty hose, dress socks, anything color coordinated went into the pile.

What remained was dark, drab and dreary. She decided she liked it that way. Her path had been narrowed even further. If people couldn't see the love in her heart for the Lord and Savior or the love and concern for them and their souls, they were looking in the wrong place. What she hoped God would see when He looked at her was a sincere heart to try to live a Godly life.

Kizzy looked at the mountain of cast off clothing and accessories, not sure what to do with it. She lay on her bed and put an arm over her eyes. If she didn't think it was worth keeping, maybe she should just burn it. Would that be a wasteful sin?

The world was going to continue to be the world even though she was changing drastically. She would take it to the homeless shelter. Maybe in her time there she could be of some influence towards getting folks away from the world. Maybe just a little.

Kiz felt herself starting to doze off. She knew she shouldn't, but it had caught her off guard. She was going under.

~II~

Kiz was driving through an endless maze of upscale neighborhoods. She saw part of what was being idolized. Energy guzzling homes. That's why we needed so much power. Decisions, decisions. Brick or stone? What color of siding? Shutters or no shutters? Fake, of course. Roofing material? All perfectly color coordinated. Concrete driveways. Three and four-car attached garages. Weed free lawns. Professional landscaping. Yards and yards of mulch. Every inch perfectly groomed. Mile after mile.

Riding lawn mowers. Snow blowers. Decks with perfect furniture: umbrellas, gas grills. Huge swingsets with forts and ladders and slides. Picket fences that served no purpose. Rare and unusual trees and bushes. Golf clubs. Tennis racquets. Weed-eaters. Perfection on a quarter acre lot.

Death and desolation stood out like a sore thumb. Nothing moving anywhere. No people, no dogs, no kids, no birds. It was all for looks, not to be used.

She looked into the dark houses. Nightlights burning everywhere. Forlorn and lonely dogs curled up on couches and rugs. Gloom. Collections of movies, books, music, toys, candles, electronic devices, food, wine, glitzy, perfectly decorated homes. But no people.

Where were they, Kiz wondered. Everything you could possibly ever want and no one home. Were they shopping for more stuff? Working? Sweating at the gym? Running their kids around to never ending activities? Dance, softball, martial arts, swimming, piano lessons, cub scouts, girl scouts, the zoo, movies, gymnastics, museums, art classes, play dates, soccer, football, basketball, baseball?

She was being shown that we idolize everything. Plans, dreams, ideas, concepts, open floor plans, master suites, privacy, in-law suites, garden tubs and

S.S. Riley

fireplaces that were never used, slate, granite, marble, porceline, stainless steel, tile, carpet, paint color, stain color, draperies, blinds, matching fabrics, towel sets, shower curtains, mirrors, comfort, air conditioning, recirculated air, jobs, prestige, money, vacations, foreign lands, mountains, shores, hardwood, drywall, paneling, wallpaper, lighting, retirement, golf, sports, education.

Excess alright. The list was endless. And were we content with any of it? No. We always had to have more, better, other, upgrades, bigger, newer. It was never going to stop. Well, she couldn't say never. God was going to end it one day. What part of "do not covet" didn't we understand?

We might say we believed in God, but it showed nowhere. He would fill us if we truly believed. Kiz didn't think we did. We were empty without God filling us, and our chasing after the elusive fulfillment we desired was leading us in the wrong direction. She could see how many voids we were trying to fill by what we had and what we wanted.

We appeared to be living like some kind of royalty, but in all actuality she could see that we were paupers. Rich wannabees. Bankrupt financially, emotionally, physically, spiritually. We were miserable. Inside and out. When the Bible said we couldn't serve two masters, did It take into account the thousands we would end up serving? Or was the mammon master just considered everything in the world?

And we weren't giving any thought at all to what the earth was suffering because of our greed. Did we think our gods of stone and metal and plastic just grew on trees? As long as the earth gave up everything we demanded, we pretended to care about it. Recycle a little here and there, reuse a few of the thousands of bags we brought our stuff home in. As long as we were comfy and satiated with everything our little hearts desired, we were good with God.

But if we lacked even one little thing, we were on our knees begging for it. We had turned ourselves into a bunch of pampered, demanding, selfish sissies.

> *Even from the days of your fathers ye are gone away from*
> *Mine Ordinances, and have not kept them. Return unto Me,*
> *and I will return unto you, saith the Lord of hosts. But ye said,*

Wherein shall we return?"
Malachi 3:7

"and discern between the righteous and the wicked,
between him that serveth God, and him that
serveth Him not."
Malachi 3:18

"So I gave them up unto their own heart's lust: and
they walked in their own counsels."
Psalm 81:12

Yep, we worshipped self. God gave people up before; Kiz wouldn't put it past Him to do it again. She remembered many times back in the "good old days" when the Lord would try to nudge her towards Him, but she backed away.

She was so busy with so many things. Mostly partying. She would feel the thought go through her mind that she needed to get back to the Bible and on her knees, but there just wasn't time. The world wouldn't give her time. The truth was, she didn't bother to make time. Now she regretted it. Day after day after day, the Lord was kept on the back burner. Had He been there stewing the whole time? Or had He returned when she decided to return to Him? What if she had died before she made that decision? What if she hadn't made it at all?

Kizzy realized in her dream how much she had changed. All of this stuff and unending activity was beginning to appall her. When was it she had reached to pull the Lord to the forefront? She didn't even know. Somehow He was off that back burner and brightly lit in her heart. But all was not well. Not yet.

Kiz woke up sobbing. At first she didn't know why. Slowly it dawned on her that something had been building inside her. Like not realizing the vague discomfort you'd been having in your jaw the last three days was a toothache coming on. There had been a foreboding playing at her for quite some time. An uneasiness that grew unnoticed. A tension that couldn't be explained. It bordered on evil calamity, doom, ugly, fearful.

There was no way she could even begin to put a finger on it. But it was bad. Something terrible was happening and she had no idea what.

As she tried to cope with the fact that something awful was wrong and if it was God's Will to inform her, He would; she felt a release come over her.

She would gladly do whatever the Spirit asked of her. She was willing to be molded. Kiz inventoried herself: her feelings, her thoughts, her motives, her emotions, her attitude. She was confident. There was no "stuff" she wouldn't push away if the Lord asked her. She didn't feel any anxiousness or resentment over anything that would be lost.

Kizzy wiped her eyes and got off the bed to start bagging up her belongings for the homeless shelter. Regardless of what was going on inside of her, life continued.

Chapter 22

"and anoint thine eyes with eye salve, that
thou mayest see."
In Revelation 3:18

Howard glanced at the clock on his office wall. The day was almost over. Twenty more minutes and he would begin his ritual. He crossed his legs on his desk and clasped his hands behind his neck.

He was a lucky, lucky man. Howard smiled. God had blessed him richly and he was thankful. There was nothing he or his family needed. They lived lavishly and Howard knew Who to thank for it.

He had power and respect. He had wealth beyond his wildest imagination. He had loyal employees and brown-nosers. He had command in high places. And it was done. Yesterday. He had everything he could ever want.

Sure, some of the products the company produced were controversial. It was to be expected. It wasn't the norm yet, but it would be. They were reaching out to make the world a better place. It needed to be better. The ones who protested, (the little people), were just misinformed. Backward maybe. His products were there to help them, too. They just couldn't see it.

But for the benefit of the wider community, they had to be silenced. And there were ways. Money was the main trick. Throw enough cash at the big mouths and they would hush. He'd seen it hundreds of times. Anyone could be bought. Except him. He stood strong for what he believed.

Howard had power everywhere he went. He was a deacon in his Church and attended every meeting. He voiced his opinions and people listened. He single-handedly paid for the new education wing, bought new robes for the choir, new hymn books for the pews. He was something alright. The best there was. Kind and generous and loved. Everyone who knew him loved him. Except for a few and they didn't matter.

His family was perfect. Beautiful, young, sexy wife. His kids from a previous marriage were well behaved and polite...all he had to do was promise them something and they fell right into line with his wishes. What could be better?

And one of their products was used by almost everyone. See...the smart ones knew it made life so much easier. It wasn't the company's fault that people used a little too much and nothing would grow on their land for years. They should read the directions better. They were printed clearly on every container. It was their own fault, not the company's.

Howard glanced at the clock again. It was blurry, but it was time. He rubbed his eyes. What was this on his hands? Some kind of scales? Did he have fish for lunch? Howard couldn't remember.

He made his way from his office through the penthouse suite to the nearest bathroom. He splashed water on his face and in his eyes, then he washed his hands. Using one of the luxurious Egyptian cotton, snow white towels, he dried himself and threw the towel onto the floor in a corner. One of the maids would pick it up.

That was better, he could see now. Odd, the water he had splashed on the sink and counter seemed to give off an eerie, lime green glow. Very faintly, but he could swear he saw it. Must be his imagination. Weird though.

Howard got on the elevator to the roof of his very own office building. The tallest tower in the city. All his. And full of hundreds of employees who were there to do his bidding. Run the business, field complaints, pay people off, take orders, take care of bills and paychecks, keep records, balance the accounts. Headquarters for factories world-wide. It was a grand business the Lord had seen fit to put into Howard's charge. He was eternally grateful.

When the elevator door opened and he stepped out onto the roof, it was raining. He liked rain; it washed his products off the plants and would then soon be reapplied. More sales, more money. Always good.

Howard walked to his favorite spot to view his empire. Mountains off to the left in the distance, then the valley with the river running through it. After that, on the right, gently rolling hills leading to flat farmland. What a spectacular view.

Howard's chest swelled with pride. Everywhere, people were using his products. Anywhere there was land there was potential. All his for the taking. He made a mental note to ramp up advertising. He had a whole crew of clever, really smart, intuitive daydreamers he could count on to come through, advance the agenda.

As he took deep breaths of satisfaction, he noticed the strange green glow again. Darker, more dense in some areas, thinning out here and there, but it seemed to be everywhere. Howard held out his hand to catch some raindrops. Yes, vaguely, like the water in the bathroom. He looked closer. It was the same.

He watched as what seemed to be microscopic green particles were absorbed into his hand. He was mesmerized and terrified at the same time. What was going on? Maybe he'd had too many martinis for lunch. He brushed his hand on his dress pants, took one last sweeping look at the landscape and headed for home.

Good thing it was Friday. Howard was sure he just needed some rest. That was it. Strange things happened when you were tired.

~II~

Howard pulled the black Mercedes out of the private garage in the basement of his office tower. That green stuff was falling on the windshield and hood. He turned on the wipers. Then he turned on the radio. Maybe he had missed something. Maybe something happened that he wasn't aware of yet. Nothing on the radio about glowing water. Same old boring news and songs he'd heard a thousand times. He turned it off. Maybe this was all his imagination; but if it was, it was a real doozy. Maybe someone slipped something into his lunch.

He drove out of the city into the hill country. He pulled the car over on a small bridge. Jumping the guardrail, Howard skidded down the embankment towards a small stream. The rain had picked up, but he didn't notice.

Just what he thought. The stream was glowing eerily. Howard put his hands on his hips and quickly surveyed the scene. He wasn't exactly sure if it was actually glowing or if it was evaporation he was witnessing. Either way, he didn't like it.

Kneeling on the bank, Howard slowly and carefully lifted a small, flat stone and waited for the sediment to clear. Nothing. He lifted another. Waited… nothing. On his third try he hit the jackpot. A crawdad nestled down into the hole left by the stone.

Bringing his hand in slowly from it's back, he seized the creature and examined it closely. What in the world? Howard could see its inner workings. The liquid pumping throughout its tiny body was green with a ghoulish glow. Was this normal for a crawdad? He didn't know. He flipped the critter over. There were dark greenish brown splotches in different places throughout. It chilled him to the bone.

He set the little guy back onto the creekbed. A green film was settling everywhere. What is this crap? Howard headed upstream, climbing over a fallen tree. He looked into the crater created by the disturbed root system. Minnows liked a little deeper, shady water. Yes. There they were. Darting back and forth, all facing the same direction. Just like when he was a boy.

Howard peered closely. Misshapen eyes, raw looking spots, the same green coursing through their bodies. He knew fish had red blood, he had cleaned enough of them. Looking closer, he could see that the green was miniscule particles suspended in the blood. Why was there so much of it? Where had it come from? And why could he see their insides?

Glancing around he noticed thicker clouds of green, glowing darker than the water. It looked like fog. Howard started walking towards it.

Where rainwater was running into the stream it appeared much darker green than the stream itself. It reminded him of dripping food coloring down the inside of a glass of water; swirling until it all became a weaker color. It creeped him out. He needed more information. Checking his watch, he headed back to his car. There had to be someone he could talk to about this.

~II~

Svetlana was curled up on the couch when he got home. She was looking at a magazine, sipping at a glass of white wine. He kissed her and went to the shower. Same faintly glowing green water. Very pale, but unmistakable.

~II~

Howard had thought that the way Svetlana pushed on her right side with the heel of her hand was just a cute habit. Now he was seeing it for what it was. He could see into her, too. Not in an obnoxious, peeping-Tom sort of way, but the same as with the minnows and crawdads. The insides.

There were greenish-brown sores on something inside her. An organ or something. Howard wasn't sure what it was. Something was wrong; very wrong. She needed to see a doctor as soon as possible. He would make the call Monday.

He tried to be pleasant as the cook served dinner. Steak, lobster, salad, green beans, diced potatoes and fresh fruit salad. It smelled wonderful, but as the lids were lifted, the glow escaped.

The lobster glowed the darkest green, followed by the salad. The steak was disgusting. Seasoned well, cooked perfectly. It was the glow. A seemingly simmering mix of gray, green and putrid yellow. Cook waited at the end of the table smiling proudly, expecting the customary gush of much felt appreciation.

Howard thanked her warmly and smiled. It wasn't her fault. She disappeared into the kitchen with a curtsy. Svetlana was digging in voraciously. Apparently he was the only one who could see this emanation. Sickened, he made his excuses and went to bed. He really wasn't feeling well and wondered if he would ever be able to eat again.

He was grateful they didn't have a dog. Not even a dog should eat that stuff. Howard didn't want to be seeing what he was seeing.

~II~

After a restless night of bad dreams where different life forms, all glowing green, were chasing after him, Howard awoke to a bright, beautiful Saturday morning. He lay on the bed watching his beautiful wife get ready for a day of shopping with her friends. The heel of her right hand kept pushing on her side. In a heartbreaking, gut wrenching moment of realization, Howard knew no doctor would be able to help her. It was just a matter of time. As she turned and moved, he could see how extensive the damage really was. What had caused this? Howard wished he knew.

When Svetlana left with a huge smile on her face, Howard scrambled to get dressed. He took the Lexus and headed out of the mountains into the farmland.

Roger had been his best friend all through school. Roger always knew he wanted to be a farmer, work in agriculture, make his living off the land. After high-school graduation, they had a double wedding. Each marrying his high-school sweetheart. Roger's marriage lasted, Howard's didn't. As Howard entered college, Roger entered the love of his life, the earth.

Howard's three children came in rapid succession. They were grown now, all in their twenties. Roger and Becca never had a child until late in life. Little

Bonnie was five now and no one thought she'd make it that far. There were problems with the pregnancy from the start. Becca had to spend the last three months in bed. Bonnie spent the first three months of her life in the hospital. After many surgeries and treatments and a "that's all we can do for her," she was sent home to die. But she hadn't…yet. It was all still up in the air. No one was making any promises.

Howard had helped with everything; hospital bills, paying farm hands and house help, giving Roger all of the products he needed for free. Anything Roger and Becca needed, Howard was there.

As he drove towards their farm, Howard knew for a fact that he cared more about that little family than he did his own. Maybe, just maybe, Roger would be able to shine a little light on what Howard had started experiencing yesterday. He tried to remember how it had begun. There was no recollection. Probably too many drinks at lunch.

Howard turned off the road onto the long gravel drive. He had tried to talk Roger into letting him have it paved, but Becca wouldn't hear of it. It was part of the charm of the life she wanted. Part of being on a farm.

He made his way slowly because of ruts and holes. When he pulled up to the house, he realized the old pickup wasn't there. Maybe someone was home. Four dogs started barking. No one came out. Howard knocked half-heartedly, not expecting an answer. He sat on a chair on the porch and looked around.

Bonnie's swing was swaying softly back and forth, hanging from a branch of an apple tree. He smiled to think of her frail body being pushed on it.

As the dogs' barking and excitement faded and they lay on the porch and in the grass, an odd noise reached his ears. It started as a low hum, then progressed to what he could only describe as a funeral dirge. He stiffened. Had something happened to Bonnie? Is that why no one was here? Was this a premonition or something? He got chills.

He strained to hear where the noise was coming from. Off to the left where the fields started. He raised himself and walked slowly in that direction. It got louder as he went. The glow was there. Darker, more dense. Howard's shoulders slumped. Roger was out spraying. The dirge was coming from what had been sprayed.

Howard fell on his knees and looked closely. The plants were drenched in poison. He could see their roots in the dirt, sucking up green where wholesome nutrients should be. The plants were diseased and deformed, tortured and suffering.

For the first time ever, Howard saw that they were living beings, not just a commodity. They had life. God had given them life. They were struggling to grow as it was their God-given duty to do. Where they should have been singing their glorious praises to God their Creator, they were weeping, crying out in their torture, torment and agony.

Worms, beetles, moths and flies writhing on the ground in pain. All dying. It was spreading to all creation. Howard's heart was breaking with compassion. He wanted more than anything to be able to wash them off, save them, put those dying things in a safe place, tell them it would be okay now. But he couldn't; there were too many, there was too much, there was no safe place for them to be. He knew it was everywhere. He had made sure of that. Birds, deer, rabbits, foxes, o'possums, groundhogs, fish, crawdads. Everything. All of them singing their mournful, melancholy death songs to God.

What scared him the most was that he knew the Creator was listening. He could hear their moans and their last gulp of breath as they died. Howard's heart yearned to comfort them somehow, but he knew it was too late for them. There was nothing he could do. He knew at that moment where all of the glowing green had come from and why it was he that was seeing it.

The scales. The ones that were on his hands when he rubbed his blurry eyes. Why was he seeing it at this point in time? After all these years? Why now?

He had been deceived. He had been listening to the wrong voices. Why did those little people have to shut up when his minions had thrown money at them? Why didn't they refuse it and scream louder? He knew why and it was all his fault.

"Damn you, Satan, damn you!" he screamed from his knees with his fists clenched towards heaven. Tears streamed down his face as he realized what he had been doing. A low, rumbling laugh reverberated through him. And it wasn't his. He vomited in disgust.

Howard was filled with remorse.

He knew what he had to do.

But he couldn't.

If it was too late, he wouldn't have been shown these things. He was being given a chance to fix it.

He had to stop it before it was too late.

He knew he had to stop it.

He had the power.

He could do it.

But he couldn't.

Too many people depended on the company for their livelihoods. Tens of thousands. Probably closer to hundreds of thousands worldwide. And the public that owned stock. And his reputation. And the government he had paid off. And his dignity. And his pride. And his bills. What would the world think?

He knew exactly what he had to do.

But he couldn't do it.

Howard forced himself to his feet and staggered on rubbery legs back to the chair on Roger's porch. What was he going to do now?

~II~

Howard wasn't sure how long he sat with his head in his hands, but the minutes dragged on in his agony. He felt vibrations before he heard the tractor coming. The scene before him unfolded as if in slow motion, every detail forever imprinted on his soul.

Roger was nearing the barn on his tractor. He looked older, weary, worried. The once majestic sprayer he pulled behind him was sneering evilly. Like some sort of villain who had won. It was the best money could buy. The cream of the crop, the god of all gods.

When Howard bought it for Roger, he believed it was the answer to every problem Roger was having. It had stood gleaming, shining in all it's glory, waiting for its proud new owner to put it into action.

Now it looked offensive, dangerous. It's long spray arms raised in victory. Glowing dark lime green, dripping with death.

When Roger saw Howard, he raised his arm and smiled. He was still a way off, chugging towards the barn. As he slowly drew closer, the old pickup came down the drive raising a brown dust cloud, glowing green around the edges. Roger turned the tractor off at the same moment the passenger door opened. Little Bonnie with her flaming red pigtails, lumbered as fast as she could toward her daddy on the tiny leg braces.

Howard wanted to scream NO!, but he was frozen. Roger was glowing from head to foot. A dark concentration of spray was around his nose and mouth. He could see it had built up in Roger's airways, sinus cavities, esophagus, lungs, stomach, intestines. It was being absorbed into his blood, tissues, muscles, bones. Dark greenish-brown spots were everywhere inside his body.

Bonnie glowed the same greenish-brown. In her bones, her heart, her brain. Roger scooped her up, twirled her around, held her in a bear hug and kissed her on the cheek. Fresh green started to glow on the child. Roger carried her to her mother's side and put his free arm across Becca's back. As they walked towards him smiling and talking, Howard could see the disease in Becca, too.

S.S. Riley

In her breasts, her lungs, her stomach and what he believed to be her reproductive organs. That horrid brown with a green glow.

~II~

Howard remembered nothing about talking to the dying little family. He was beyond grieving. He was mortified, paralyzed with fear. There was panic as he had never known panic before. What was he going to do? He turned up the radio as loud as it would go to drown out the dirge. Faster and faster he drove, but there was no getting away. He floored the car and shut his eyes to block out the ghastly green glow that was all around him.

~II~

Three hikers stood watching as a wrecker pulled a silver Lexus out of the river. They had spotted what they believed to be a car submerged in the muddy water. Sure enough, there it was. It was a gruesome sight for them to see a man's lifeless body bobbing around in the driver's seat. What they couldn't see was the glow.

> *"And with all deceivableness of unrighteousness in them*
> *that perish; because they received not the love of the truth,*
> *that they might be saved."*
> *2 Thessalonians 2:16*

Chapter 23

"worship God."
In Revelation 22:9

Kizzy wasn't 100% sure what it meant to worship anything. The words in the dictionary didn't do any sort of justice to what it must mean to worship God. She wanted to, with all her heart. And she knew she couldn't learn it alone. Maybe she could learn by watching others. But, so far, that hadn't worked.

Once again the yearning was growing in her to be with fellow believers. Her heart was still with the poverty stricken people in the area of the Church, but she promised herself she would never go back. So she started looking.

Kiz made several trips up and down the streets, looking and reading Church signs. Nothing jumped out at her, so she went home and prayed. A few days later, after returning from another scouting trip, the decision was made for her. She was to go back to the same Church she had walked out of on All Saints' Day.

It certainly wasn't what SHE would have chosen and was not what she wanted to do. But she didn't argue. She would go. It would be good to see the small family she had left behind. It would be good to see the group that came to eat.

Even though she believed the pastor was a false teacher, she would go. Maybe things had changed. She could filter out and investigate anything that didn't feel right. If it was where the Spirit was sending her, it would be futile to go elsewhere. There must be a reason for it.

Kizzy smiled and shook her head when she found out what day it was that the Lord sent her back. Two years to the day. Well, almost. It was All Saints' Day. She could feel that it was no coincidence. There was definitely a reason. She settled in and made the best of it.

The organ music and the old hymns set her soul afire. It was truly beautiful and moving. Maybe this was worship. She could feel the Spirit in her. Kiz didn't want it to end.

But of course it did. She wasn't very fond of the get-up-and-greet-people part. It seemed to intrude on the mental preparation to focus all attention on the Lord. People were always continuing their conversations from before the service started. Usually health-related or current events topics. Kiz would rather not participate, but she did.

"O priests, that despise My Name."
In Malachi 1:6

Things had changed alright. And not for the better. Many times she questioned God. Are you sure I should be here? Are you sure this is where you want me to be? The answer was always "Yes."

One of those times was when the preacher was highly praising the wisdom of the Buddhists. He read another lengthy praise creation poem, not even mentioning the Creator. He had put an insert in the bulletin. It was a Psalm from a "very special" version of the Bible. He had the whole congregation read it aloud together.

She sensed something fishy and when she got home, she compared the insert to what was written in her good-old King James Version. It didn't surprise her a bit to find that everywhere the KJV said "the Lord," the very special version had taken those two words out and replaced them with "what is."

Where it should have said "trust the Lord," the paper read "trust what is." It curdled her stomach. Her brothers and sisters were swallowing it down, not questioning anything. Needless to say, Kiz was on her toes at all times.

She was sick of feel-good messages. She didn't want flowery, poetic sermons or tall tales. She wanted the truth. She was tired of hearing that whatever she did or thought was okay. Go for it. If it makes you feel good, do it. God wants you to feel good.

Kiz knew that not everything she did was okay; it wasn't. She wanted to be convicted, convinced of the truth. She wanted, no - needed, guidance. She needed to hear the truth so the Word would change her life. But she wasn't getting it here. She hadn't gotten it in any Church so far.

Kiz was absolutely sure that things were evil in this "church." No one else seemed to notice anything wrong. She believed Christians were in a spiritual battle every single day of their lives. Evil was constantly attacking us. If we were to be completely passive, it would swallow us whole. We needed the armour of God. The fight may be His, but we were always asked to do something. We are involved in a battle and we must fight. We can't just cave in to sinister activity. We would soon become overwhelmed.

So many times she wanted to open her mouth, but her discernment said to wait. The time would come. Her mouth would be opened soon enough.

> *"A little leaven leaveneth the whole lump."*
> *Galatians 5:9*

After her second return visit to the Church, Kiz fell back into the outreach programs. She enjoyed it before and was happy to see all of the faces from the surrounding community. She had missed them badly.

One face was new, a little African-American woman named Charlie. Kiz had never seen her before. She wasn't at Sunday services, but she seemed to be running the outreach programs. Running the show. From the first two hours she spent with her that first Saturday, Kiz knew something was wrong. Actually, a lot of things were wrong.

The sanctuary, foyer, bathrooms and dining hall were presentable. But the rest of the church was trashed. A refrigerator they used to store food was warm. It held a running temperature of 65 degrees. There was moldy, smelly food in it along with the fresh items that had just been brought in. The water fountain was broken.

Food storage areas were piled up with garbage. There were mouse droppings everywhere.

There was no place for visiting children to go. There seemed to be a need for parents to have at least a clean, safe place for their children to play when they came for services. There was nothing for them but a piled up rat hole.

Old fixtures, bags and boxes of used clothing, tarps, paint cans, broken and bent hangers, empty cardboard boxes with dirt and trash in them and a few broken toys thrown into the mix. Not one inch of the Church was off limits to the people who came in off the streets for meals. Obviously, no one cared that it was a Church.

And then there was Charlie. For six months Kiz worked the meals. Charlie proved more and more to be a warden in some sort of prison refugee camp. She screamed at guests, made kids cry, bossed people around, decided who could and couldn't take clothes or food, how much they could take and when they could take it. Plus, she was stealing everything she could get her hands on.

Kiz was getting at least half a dozen complaints about Charlie at every single meal. In the rare event Charlie didn't show up, no one complained about anything. Ever.

Also, Charlie had a table of friends that deliberately made a mess at every meal. They turned their plates over with food on them, dumped their drinks onto the food and smeared stuff all over the chairs.

Kiz couldn't understand why the pastor let her and them do the things they were doing. He acted as though they were best of friends. It must have been the old, "no matter what you do, it's okay, we love you" mentality. It wasn't okay and it didn't belong in a Church. It was obnoxious, disruptive and disrespectful.

Finally, out of the blue, the pastor announced he was leaving the Church. His aging mother in another state would be needing some help.

Kiz had to restrain herself; she wanted to jump up and down, clapping and whooping. But she didn't, of course. Things were going to change. Hopefully for the better.

> *"All Scripture is given by inspiration of God, and is*
> *profitable for doctrine, for reproof, for correction,*
> *for instruction in righteousness:"*
> *2 Timothy 3:16*

Kiz cringed as the preacher held up his copy of the Bible and confessed that there really wasn't much in it that was of any importance to him. Was this blasphemy? It deeply angered and saddened her at the same time. She knew he was speaking the truth. She had heard it in every reflection he had given. She commenced praying harder for his soul.

Then he left on a three-week vacation.

> *"Ye shall keep My Sabbaths, and reverence*
> *My Sanctuary: I Am the Lord."*
> *Leviticus 19:30*

Kizzy was thoroughly disgusted by such behavior in a so-called Church. Not only by the preacher, but also by what he allowed to happen in it. It wasn't right. There was no righteousness in it. She loved God, loved Jesus, loved the Spirit. We were supposed to keep His Temple pure and holy. She knew the body was the temple, but the Church building itself should hold some important significance. Some sort of dignity.

Kiz could feel the prompting of the Spirit and she heeded. The pastor was out of town, but he would soon be leaving the Church for good. Kiz knew he had already, in his heart, left. The next Sunday she asked for a meeting of the elders and members. After the service, everyone gathered in the dining hall.

She knew it was wrong to keep track of anyone's trespasses, we were to forgive. In her personal life she did. This was different. The members of this community were struggling with life in general. When they were invited into the Church for a meal, they should be treated kindly. The opposite was happening.

So she pulled out her list and began to read. Theft. Screaming at people. She yelled at a three-year old Laotian boy. In fear, he crawled under a table, crying. Charlie continued to yell at him for several minutes. Denying people food and clothing because she didn't like them. Yelling at innocent kids because of someone else's trash in the yard. Starting fights, gossiping about people who were quietly sitting on the other side of the room. Not letting kids in to eat because they weren't with an adult. This list went on and on.

Some people were familiar with Charlie's behavior, but most weren't. It was a general agreement that the woman's behavior had to stop. No one approved of it but the preacher. Luckily, he wasn't there to protest.

The bad part was, not many in the congregation helped at these meals. Some did, but their attendance was spotty. There were many days when Kiz was the only representative of the Church that showed up. Most of the people had no idea what had been happening. Other Churches prepared the food and brought it in. The cooking wasn't done there. So mainly it was just her word standing alone.

Kiz thought the elders would take care of the problem. It should have been them that talked to the preacher. So she was rather surprised when he called her from his vacation the next day.

After greetings were exchanged, he asked what was up. Kiz related about the meeting and the resulting decision that he should talk to Charlie and tone down her behavior before he left the Church for good.

He informed her that he was well aware of Charlie's inappropriate behavior and had been for some time. Kiz was meddling in something she knew nothing about. With so many cultural, ethnic, social and racial differences in that neighborhood, people were treated better by Charlie than they were on the streets and in their own homes. He had no intention of talking to Charlie, thank you, and was dismissing entirely the wishes of the elders and members because of the source. He resented his leadership being attacked.

He then informed her that she had misplaced reverence for the Church, she was misinformed, stirring up trouble where there was none and he felt sorry for her. He would be praying for her because she desperately needed it. She did agree with that last part. Kiz said she would be praying for him also and quickly hung up.

Immediately she texted him that God destroyed His Own Temple because of the actions of the people. She wouldn't put it past Him to do it again and we needed to be very careful. She never got an answer to that text.

> *"Moreover it is required in stewards,*
> *that a man be found faithful."*
> *1 Corinthians 4:2*

Kizzy expected to see shocking behavior on the streets and in the news, but the truth was she had seen more in the Churches than she had anywhere else.

The preacher knew Charlie was stealing. The board president told her it had been going on for a long time. Years in fact. So, if the board president knew, too, didn't that make both of them just as guilty as Charlie? They were part and parcel in the damage that was being done.

Yes, Judas was a thief, but we aren't Jesus. Were we supposed to let a person treat people poorly and rob the Church blind? Kiz searched herself many, many times and decided she at least had to try to make it stop.

They were letting a thief steal from God. Many other Churches with the same name brand were struggling to make ends meet, but they still sacrificed to make sure there was food and clothing in the pantry in case a homeless person came needing something. And many did. Businesses and organizations gave so that those in need would be fed and clothed.

Tithes and offerings were given in good faith they would be used in an efficient and proper way. The board president may have been told and was subject to pastoral confidence. That would leave it all on the pastor's shoulders. But… the board president had told Kiz. Still, without knowing these things for sure, she had to believe it was the pastor who held full responsibility.

Many donors trusted that the pastor would use things in a Godly manner. None of it, technically, was his to let her steal. Money, food, clothing and household goods were entrusted to the Church. Not to him. Yet he continued to let her sneak bags and bags out two or three times a week. She would even steal the grape juice that was intended for communion. Sometimes she would make more than one sneak carrying things out. He did nothing to stop her. Nothing. On the contrary, he seemed to be encouraging her.

Kiz had a very similar background to many of those who came to the Church for help. Only by the Grace of God was she not still in a vicarious position. As time wore on, many of the neighbors started to trust her with their life stories, complaints and gossip.

She heard from several unrelated sources that what Charlie took from the Church was sold so she would have money for drugs and alcohol. If the preacher knew this, he was an enabler of the worst kind. He might as well be handing her the drugs and alcohol himself. Kiz was sure he knew. He had to. But in her gut she felt as if he didn't really care.

As far as she was concerned, he owed many, many apologies. But he wasn't likely to give them.

He owed an apology to the community for allowing Charlie to treat them badly and for letting her steal huge amounts of stuff that was donated for their benefit.

He owed an apology to the Church for misuse and breach of trust. Plus, Charlie was giving the Church a bad name in the "hood". Many people who needed help refused to come because of her.

He owed an apology to God most of all, for not being a good steward of all that was put into his hands and for the disrespect and abuse he allowed to occur.

He owed an apology to anyone who donated believing things were being put to good use.

He owed an apology to Charlie, too, for letting her think her sinful behavior was okay and not warning her of the consequences of her actions.

Kizzy gave all she could on top of her tithes. She was by no means well-off, but she felt called to help people. They needed it more than she did.

What she brought was meant to be given to people. Not stolen and then sold to those who needed it so someone's drug habit could be supported. She didn't want to be an enabler and hated that God's House of Worship was. What right did the pastor have to let someone steal resources that were dedicated to the Lord? How could he justify it or did it ever cross his mind? Would it ever cross his mind?

~II~

Kiz had noticed early on that there was Bible study for men one night a week, but nothing for women or mixed company. And the preacher didn't lead the study. Someone else came in to do it.

She offered to host one and it was okayed. A couple of ladies from the Church came the first three weeks and then it died out. Since she had been given a key to the front door, she began using Bible study time to clean up the Church.

Her Bible study materials were always ready in case someone showed up, but they didn't.

The warm refrigerator was unplugged and what little cold was in the freezer was allowed to thaw. As Kiz cleaned out the filth and slime, getting rid of everything it contained, she noticed that the seals in the freezer were either missing or destroyed. It appeared that some water had frozen at one point in time, pushing the liner apart.

Thinking something was better than nothing, she bought a can of spray foam insulation and filled the crevices. After a good scrubbing she plugged it back in and waited. It finally hit the safe mark on the thermometer and Kiz declared it usable.

Then she started on the dry goods storage room. There were mouse droppings and brown urine spots everywhere. In bags and boxes of paper and foam cups, in bags of foam plates and bowls, bags of plastic cutlery, in pots and pans, baskets, serving bowls. Had these items been used to feed members of the community? She believed so.

Kiz hauled carloads of just plain filth out of the tiny room. Apparently the mouse problem had been taken care of. There were none in the sticky traps. But the mess had never been touched.

She scrubbed shelves, dishes, pots, pans, and the floor. She organized things as she sorted through. What had been a cluttered, filthy, disgusting jam packed room was now presentable, clean and usable. Then she repaired the drinking fountain.

Then she turned her attention to the second refrigerator. It was full of moldy food and outdated jars of everything. Some outdated by as much as five years. She was thoroughly disgusted. What kind of responsible leadership was present? Her shoulders slumped as she realized there was none. More carloads of junk left the building.

There was a large room behind the dining hall that could be divided into four smaller rooms by using sliding curtains. She left the two front rooms open because that was where the food was served. She cleaned it well, then closed curtains to form two smaller rooms in the back. One she cleaned out, organized and used for storage. Carts full of playground toys that were never used, computers, coat racks, easels. Any miscellaneous stuff that wasn't being used.

The second small room she closed off and turned into a nursery. She put in a rocking chair and afghan. A table beside the rocking chair held a small dollhouse and a Bible. She put in a short table with some children's chairs around it.

A couple shelving units held toys, books, markers, etc. When it was finished, she put up a sign that it was closed to the public. The Church needed a place for kids of parents who wanted to attend services. Kiz used her own money to buy the toys in the nursery. She put up another sign that they were not to be included in the giveaways. More trash was taken out.

The nursery stayed closed when Kiz was there. But on days she had to work, it was opened up and ransacked. She knew exactly who was responsible for the mess, damage and missing and broken toys. The Bible disappeared along with other things. She would find her signs crumpled up on the floor. Each time the room was torn up, Kiz would clean it and fix it up with whatever toys were left.

Then came the small room that was used as the food pantry. That was where packaged food was stored. When a homeless or hungry person asked for food, this is where it was stored. It also had a cabinet with personal items. Kiz sorted out razors, can openers, reading glasses, shampoo, deodorant, diapers, etc. Mouse mess all over in here too.

She moved the used clothing out of it into the storage room she had made. Many miscellaneous items were taken out. Shelves were scrubbed and the food was arranged according to groups. The carpet was swept thoroughly. This was where Charlie did a good deal of her stealing.

It was quite a chore keeping these areas clean and orderly. No one seemed to care. Things were just thrown wherever anyone wanted to throw them. It felt sometimes as if it was purposely done, but Kiz kept after it diligently.

"I will repay, saith the Lord."
In Romans 12:19

Through the grapevine, word reached her that immediately after the preacher hung up from their conversation, he stepped off a curb, twisting his ankle and ripping a tendon in his thigh. Surgery was required to sew it back together.

Kiz wasn't sure about anything. No one asked her how their conversation went, so she assumed the preacher had told everyone HIS version of what was said. She knew his feelings about her and was pretty sure nothing good was being said about her.

Deep inside, Kiz had a bad feeling about the whole Church. She also somehow knew that this injury and upcoming surgery was being blamed on her. She hadn't cursed him in any way, and prayed for him often. What did these people believe?

Attitudes toward her were beginning to cool amongst the congregation. It was obvious. She knew the Lord wanted her to be there, so she wasn't deterred in any way except for an uncomfortable feeling around certain people. If God had sent her back, and she knew He did, there was no way she was going to walk away…not yet.

"But if ye have respect to persons, ye commit sin…"
In James 2:9

Kiz bided her time and waited until the preacher was finally gone. The farewell services and dinners broke her heart because she knew from their conversation how he felt about the congregation, dismissing their wishes because of the source. He had said things that made her think he thought they were useless to his agenda. And there he was, gloating and blushing at all of the tears, toasts, love and attention.

As soon as he was gone, Kiz started making her case against Charlie to the board. Little by little she made the wishes of the congregation and community known to them.

The first step that was taken was to lock up the food pantry. Kiz was extremely surprised to find out that the board decided to give her a key and put her in charge of it. She proposed that a trusted community volunteer share the responsibility with her. It was accepted and the woman was given a key also. Now, if Kiz wasn't present, the other woman could dole out food to whoever needed some. And it was no longer vulnerable to being stolen. If Charlie needed something, she would have to ask just like everyone else. Maybe things were gong to change after all.

Kiz was elated when the board president told her he would speak to Charlie and set some ground rules for her, as a volunteer, to follow. Her elation was short-lived however when he informed her that he hadn't talked to Charlie after all. He had only told her that Kiz was now in charge of the pantry.

This set off all kinds of fireworks and hatred. Charlie became even more belligerent and cruel. She started to throw the word "racist" around. This was absolutely not the case. Kiz didn't have a racist bone in her body. She loved everyone in the community. Even Charlie and the ex-preacher. She had African-American friends and neighbors. More than half of the people who came for meals were African-American and she got along with them all. Couldn't Charlie see that it wasn't the color of her skin that was the problem? It was her behavior.

As more and more, bigger, different and threatening problems arose, Kiz stepped up her efforts. It wasn't a case of setting rules for volunteers to follow anymore, that wasn't going to happen. Charlie had to go. Kiz spoke to board members and wrote letters detailing Charlie's increasingly bad and hateful behavior.

Everyone agreed that Charlie's actions were despicable, but no one would do anything to stop it. They let it continue. All Kiz could figure out was that it boiled down to loyalty to the former preacher. What about loyalty to Jesus? Kiz wondered if the board knew the preacher had said Charlie was one problem he wasn't taking to Virginia with him.

Kiz's discomfort deepened when she was told that the board had decided that no one was allowed into the pantry anymore unless a board member was in the building. Huh…when would that be? Two people had keys, but when a homeless person came asking for food, they had to be turned away empty-handed.

As she waited for things to happen that she was told would happen (but never did), she became, for lack of a better word, discouraged. She wondered if the board was seeking the Lord's direction in any of their decisions or if they were just flying by the seat of their pants, the way the world does. Decisions were made and not carried through or they were reversed shortly after they were made.

She had a hard time understanding any of it. They were just people after all, but they were supposed to be Christians. To her, that carried a weighty load of responsibility with it.

As Kiz became more acquainted with board ways, she realized it acted as if the Church was leaderless. With the absence of a permanent preacher, it became clear that no one could wipe their nose without board approval. What about the elders? Didn't they have any say about anything? Apparently not. The Father, Son and Holy Ghost were the leaders in her eyes and she was following. It was THEIR Church, wasn't it? Kiz prayed a lot during this time. She couldn't understand why everyone seemed to be relying so heavily on her and refusing to work with her at the same time.

"except he will first bind the strong man..."
In Mark 3:27

Yes, we were bound up tight alright. Bound up with tolerance and acceptance. It was being idolized in the face of wrong and evil. And God's House, what was supposed to be a House of Prayer, the Church building, was being ruined in the process.

Kiz could only see them as hypocrites. Would they let someone come into their houses two or three times a week, every week, and collect up so much stuff that they needed help to carry it all out? Would they let someone come into their homes and scream at other guests? Start fights? Talk nasty gossip about other guests? Threaten people? She seriously doubted it. They would stop it immediately.

Were they demanding too much respect for themselves and their property while the Only One who actually deserved respect, dignity and honor was getting none at all? Kiz was becoming ill at the ways of the world. It was genuinely making her sick. Yet she stopped questioning God as to why He had brought her back into this stinking hole. It was becoming crystal clear.

~II~

"...For this cause God gave them up unto vile affections;
for even their women did change the natural use into

that which is against nature..."
In Romans 1:27

Kizzy put her vote in several times for a fill-in preacher. He was a middle-aged African-American man with a lovely family. He had filled in on numerous occasions when the old preacher was at other Churches or out of town.

She was overridden, of course, and the lesbian preacher couple took over services. This was another aspect of the "accept and tolerate" mindset. Kiz tried hard to keep her mind off the matter. What parts of the Bible didn't they understand? She had to leave it between them and Jesus. She loved the sinners, but hated the sin. She was a sinner herself.

Nothing she could say or do was going to change their lifestyle in the least. She couldn't accept it as solid Christian behavior and often wondered if the Spirit was present during services. She had no way of knowing.

Their sermons were Bible based, which she was thankful for, but they were sometimes flowery and, of course, a lot of the sermons were centered around acceptance. Love was a favorite topic, too. At least most of them had a little substance to them.

One Sunday they announced that they were going to incorporate Church member testimony into the services. First, they asked a few people who were life-long members.

Kiz had a sinking feeling that she would be asked. Why else would God bring her back? To say nothing? Yeah, right. She didn't want to do it. When she was approached to speak, Kiz said she wasn't sure. Everything that had come to mind ended up being a sermon. She was told there were enough preachers in the Church, all they wanted was testimony.

At the Spirit's urging, Kiz reluctantly consented. She would be testifying the next week along with a young African-American man. They were both newer members of the Church.

Kizzy was actually surprised that she had been asked.

*"If the world hate you, ye know that it hated
Me before it hated you."*
John 15:18

Kiz knew she was on the verge of being ostracized by that brand name Church. It was because of her serious efforts to stop Charlie. This was a Church, for crying out loud. Why should well over a hundred people suffer abuse on a weekly basis because of one person? Her requests for help were being ignored and getting her in hot water. She was obviously standing alone on this one.

She thought it would be the "world" that hated her. Little did she know it would be her own dearly beloved brothers and sisters. Some friends from the community informed her she had been labeled a trouble-maker by the Church. It didn't surprise her a bit.

What did surprise her was the fact that the outside community loved her. They supported her efforts and thanked her often for trying to help them.

*"…take ye no thought how or what things ye shall answer,
or what ye shall say…"*
In Luke 12:11

Kiz started her testimony on paper. She crumpled it up and tossed it aside. Over and over again. Nothing felt right. In exasperation she fell on her knees and asked God what He wanted her to say.

It came. She wrote. And trembled. In her eyes, this was not good. But what can man know of the Ways of God? She felt absolutely sure it was coming from the Spirit. But she also felt that her time at that particular Church was coming to an abrupt end.

They would take it to heart and listen or they would become indignant and throw her to the lions. She prayed they would listen, but she couldn't make them.

The next Sunday Kiz felt weirdly calm in the face of what was to come. The human part of her dreaded what she would say, but she felt a sure strength carrying her. The young man that was to also speak that morning didn't show up. She would have plenty of time that she didn't really want.

The service progressed as normal until the sermon. She was introduced and walked to the podium on unsteady legs. Kiz took a deep breath and looked out at the small gathering of dearly beloved faces. Hard, stony, unfriendly faces. Unforgiving faces. All pointed directly at her.

"Good morning."

Silence until...you'll have to talk louder than that.

"Good morning," she said louder. Silence. She knew that her nerves would cause her to speak in a low, monotone voice. It had happened before. There was nothing she could do about it.

"I told Jan I would pray about this and I did. I asked God what He wanted me to say. This is the result. I'm sorry, I tried. My testimony cannot be separated from Scripture. The Great Commission is 'go and preach,' not sit and listen."

The preacher nodded and gave a half smile.

"I did not grow up in a Christian home as most of you did. In fact, at a very early age I realized I had to take care of myself because no one else was going to. I spent most of my time alone in the woods behind our house because if I went home, I would usually get beaten.

"My aunt would come occasionally and take me to her Church. That must be where the seed was planted. As I grew older I read the Bible avidly and did many studies from it. I made a few minor, temporary changes in my life. I thought I was wise and knew it all. How sad. I had no idea that my eyes were blind and my ears weren't hearing. I continued to do whatever I wanted. Horrid, sinful things. I made a huge mess of my life.

"The Lord used a murderer to start turning my life around. (gasps from the congregation.)

"My son came home from work one day, upset because he tried to stop for gas. The station was cordoned off with yellow tape. There was a dead man lying in a pool of blood in the parking lot. I read the story in the paper the next day. I could feel urgings to write to the shooter in jail. So I did. It was what I thought to be an encouraging letter.

"I told him the story of how Moses had killed an Egyptian who was beating a Hebrew slave. God eventually used Moses to lead His people out of captivity. There was hope.

" I received in return a very angry letter. At this point in time all I remember from it is that he had done community service all his life and what had I ever done to help anybody?

"It knocked me for a loop. What HAD I done for the community? For those in need? It stopped me dead in my tracks. It hit me like a ton of bricks. I believed it was at that time the Lord began to open my eyes.

"I was familiar with Scripture. A corrupt tree cannot produce good fruit. Had anything good I had ever done counted at all? If a man is on his way to rob a bank and stops to help an old lady cross a busy street, had he really done a good thing? If he then continued on, robbed the bank and killed three people, was his help to the woman in vain? Was I the same as he? Trekking my way to sinful actions before and after the good deed?

"It was then that I tried attending Church on a regular basis and immersed myself in helping the community. I sincerely prayed for my eyes, ears, heart and mind to be opened and for the Lord to impart to me any understanding He wanted me to have. It was a very scary thing when it started to happen and still is to this day. I put myself under the Authority of my Lord, King, Savior and Friend.

"I asked Him questions about what I read in the Bible. 'Be ye not conformed to this world, but be ye transformed by the renewing of your mind.' What are the things of this world, God? He told me.

S.S. Riley

"A lot of stuff went bye-bye. The biggest thing to go was the cable TV. I heard in my head the words 'it's time to start living your life instead of watching other people live lies.' From piecing Scripture together, I realized that any sort of deception was a lie. What is deceiving, God? A lot more stuff went out the door.

"One passage weighed particularly heavy on my mind. 'Not all who say, Lord, Lord, will enter the Kingdom of Heaven, but those who do the Will of My Father which is in Heaven.' What is Your Will, God? It's all in the Bible. We don't have to guess.

"I started comparing what people told me to what the Bible says. Many things are Biblically untrue. Acts 17:11 states: 'These were more noble than those in Thessalonica in that they received the Word with alll readiness of mind, and searched the Scriptures daily, whether these things were so.' I am not noble in any way, but that's what I did. We are being taught lies and we need to be vigilant.

"Some folks are very appreciative of what I am trying to do here. Last week a Church member who also lives in this impoverished neighborhood thanked me and told me I was brave. Of course, I checked the Bible. Bravery is listed once. That's all.

"Isaiah 3:18 'In that day the Lord will take away the bravery of their tinkling ornaments about their feet, and their cauls and their round tires like moons.'

"Any account in the Bible which could be attributed to bravery:

"David killing Goliath.

"Daniel in the lion's den.

"Shadrach, Meshack and Abednigo being thrown into the furnace, are all actually faith, trust, hope and confidence in the Lord. He wants and de-serves all of the glory and honor. Not for it to be given to us. Brave is a word that belongs to the world, not to Christians. Thank you, but sorry Hil, there is no bravery in me.

Deprogrammed 219

"Once when I was a child alone in the woods I very clearly heard a man's voice in my head telling me I was going to do something important. At the time, I didn't take it as a calling. I instinctively knew it was referring to the future.

"How could God use a huge sinner like me to accomplish anything? Let alone something important? I've been questioning it for years. Last week in her sermon Sue said, 'God doesn't use perfect people. It's not about you. Obey. Reflect God in all that you are.'

"What Jan read from Jeremiah drove home what I've only just begun to realize:

" ' See, I have this day set Thee over the nations and over kingdoms, to root out, and to pull down, and to destroy, and to throw down, to build and to plant.' "

"Yes, it is about Jesus, but if His Spirit dwells in us, He is there. I have gotten a lot of flack for trying to get evil out of this Church. I've been told by more than a few people that the building is nothing. The Kingdom of God is within us. I disagree wholeheartedly that the Church building itself is nothing. If it means nothing, why do we even bother to do it? Why do we spend so much money to build it and put up a sign out front calling it a Church? Why bother?

"Because it is supposed to be a symbol of all that is Holy. Righteous and Pure. Can we have misplaced reverence for a building that is supposed to be a Church? Only if we have no reverence at all for what it represents.

"Sue also said last week that we are in an evil and perverse generation as never before. There are a great many ungodly people in the world. That's not to say they always will be, but at this point in time, they are. We need to pray hard.

"Jan wanted me to talk about my ministry, the Bible study. A few came for the first three weeks, then no one. I used that time to clean up the Church. Ann wanted to come, but had to work. Week after week I came prepared,

S.S. Riley

but no one showed up. That's okay because my reason for being here goes much wider and deeper than that."

Kiz stopped and looked into each face she adored.

"I love you all very much, but it was not my choice to come back here last year. I was sent. This Church is dwindling away fast and needs help badly. If we don't do something, as it says in Jeremiah, 'root out, pull down, destroy and throw down,' there will be no building or planting. This Church is at a turning point. It will go one of two ways. Up or down. We haven't been set over nations or kingdoms, but over this building, this Church."

When I got to this point I panicked and pleaded 'Lord, these dearly loved brothers and sisters are going to run me out of the Church. Please don't ask me to do this. Please.'

Right then I was given a vision of a breeze blowing through ancient trees. It only lasted about three seconds. The thought "Holy Breeze" came into my mind. Later that evening I was reading a book on discipleship. It stated that the wind is a symbol of the Spirit. I believe I had been refreshed by the Spirit.

"I can disobey, but the consequences will not be good. So I won't, regardless of what earthly things are going to happen.

"The life and the growth of this Church depends on three things. First, we have let an ungodly woman put herself in a position of authority over every single outreach program that we have. She needs to go. Respect needs to be shown for what this building represents."

There were angry noises and indignant hmphs coming from the organist. Kiz chose to ignore them.

"Second, I am confident that if the Lord has asked me to do this, He has already laid the groundwork. The Lord improves us as we walk with Him. He changes our lives. It's called 'purifying' in the Bible. If something has been put on our conscience that we are neglecting to do, now is the time to do it.

"The Lord wants to see growth in us before there will be growth in the Church. It could be more time in prayer, more time reading God's Word, something we need to start doing or something we need to stop doing. We each know what the Lord is asking us to do."

Louder angry noises and hmphs.

"Third, we need to eagerly be prepared to give God the praise, honor and glory if and when the Church does start to turn around. He is a jealous God and is the Only One worthy and deserving of that praise.

"If he indeed decides to send that young pastor who they say is on fire for the Word of God, we need to thank HIM for that, not lay all of the praise on the young man as we have been doing so far. We can't give the praise and glory to anyone but God. As the Body of Christ, we need to step up to the plate and make the way straight for the Lord. The Glory of God demands it. Thank you."

~II~

As Kiz returned to her pew, she heard one person clapping. She didn't look to see who it was. She could feel in her heart that her work here was done. She knew she wouldn't be returning.

> "...so He shall open, and none shall shut; and He
> shall shut, and none shall open."
> In Isaiah 22:22

There was a young man fresh out of seminary that was being considerd as the new preacher for the Church. His portfolio of earthly experience glowed, especially the parts about applying for and receiving grants. It was said he was on fire for the Word of God, but Kiz had seen no evidence of that when he was around. The whole small congregation was enamored and excited about what HE was going to do for the Church. He was actually the only candidate for the job. The excitement hadn't reached Kiz. For some reason she only felt an air of foreboding.

The Sunday following her testimony was to be the day for his trial sermon. Everyone was to come and bring any questions they had. Kiz had plenty.

Do you use "very special" versions of the Bible?

Are you dabbling in other religions that you will be incorporating into the services?

Do you think elderly people are useless, contribute nothing and are just sitting around waiting to die?

Do you only want Annas and Ezekials in YOUR Church?

Would you ever have the audacity to hold up a Bible and confess there really wasn't much in it that was of any importance to you?

Would you consider overriding the wishes of the elders and members of the Church because you didn't like confrontation and they weren't furthering your agenda?

Whose Church is this?

Do you refuse to perform legal weddings between a man and a woman until anyone who wants to get married can?

Do you believe it is okay for someone to continually steal resources dedicated to the work of the Lord?

The list went on and on. She had a lot of legitimate questions that needed honest answers. But she wouldn't be there to ask them - troublemaker that she was.

The next Sunday morning Kiz didn't go to Church at all. She dressed in black, went down by the lake in the impoverished area and mourned the death of the Church.

Chapter 24

"…which go a whoring after their idols…"
In Ezekial 6:9

"…but pollute ye My Holy Name no more with your
gifts, and with your idols."
In Ezekial 20:39

"…which went astray from Me after their idols;
they shall even bear their iniquity."
In Exekial 44:10

A few weeks after her departure, Kiz found she had some donations to take to her friends and acquaintances who live by her ex-Church. Where she was going took her directly past it.

Her eyesight wasn't what it used to be, so she was quite near before she could read the sign in front of the Church. Her breath caught, her stomach knotted and her eyes began to sting. "Oh, precious Jesus, I am so sorry." It didn't take her by surprise at all. She somehow expected it, but still, it was a huge jolt to her system. Her instincts about the Church had been right.

Perfectly, meticulously centered and spaced, she read:

BUDDHIST
MEDITATION

A day and time were shown, but she didn't read that far.

~II~

My dearest Laura,

Hello. I know I am not welcome anymore, but I want you to know I love you and your little family dearly. I miss all of you at the Church. I have been praying that the Lord would open someone's eyes and your name keeps coming to mind. Please, Laura, please, pray and ask God to make you understand what is happening.

There are a thousand things that young preacher could have offered to the neighborhood, all Biblical, serving the Kingdom of God. But he offers idol worship? Buddhist meditation? Oh, my heart breaks for you all. If someone doesn't put their foot down and make this blasphemy stop, you are all guilty.

Please, Laura, consider breaking away from that brand name of Church. Run as far away as fast as you can go. Take as many brothers and sisters with you as will go. I know you think I am crazy and a troublemaker, but seriously think about what is going on. Don't condone it, Laura, don't accept it. Your very souls may be in jeopardy.

In Christian love,
Kizzy

Chapter 25

"Six days may work be done; but in the Seventh is the
Sabbath of rest, Holy to the Lord: whosoever doeth any
work in the Sabbath Day, he shall surely be
put to death."
Exodus 31:15

The seventh day. The seventh…hmm…Something was building within Kiz's being. Not sure exactly what yet, she got on her knees and waited in silence. She waited, remaining quiet and trying to expel any day-to-day thoughts that tried to creep in. Listening…waiting…

There it was. The week END! The end of the week. Two ends actually. The front end and the back end. Saying her thanks, but not quite knowing what for yet, she headed to her calendar. Staring, scanning, she kept the God receptors open.

At first the month just looked like a bunch of squares all pushed together, telling us what day it was. Then something she knew hit her with fresh clarity. It was divided into weeks. A line of seven days for each week.

Kiz always knew that where God was concerned, everything was set in stone. Designed in a certain way for His Divine Purposes. The calendar included. She swallowed hard.

She stared off into space, not seeing anything really, just a blur. What the…? It was right there as plain as the big nose on her face. She'd heard many times over the years that Jewish people observed the Sabbath on Saturday. She never thought about it one way or the other until now. One of those "being blinded" things she guessed. We did know best, didn't we?

Too much going on to pay any attention to it…until now. Now. A revelation was being given to her at this very moment. She smiled. Not worthy and she knew it. Thank You, Lord.

Looking at the calendar again, she realized the Jews were right. Sunday was the first day of the week. Saturday was the seventh. She counted. Yes. It was the seventh. There was no way a mistake could have been made. It was simple. What was going on? If Sunday was the seventh day, the Sabbath, the calendar would have been designed to depict it, the week would have started with Monday.

For most people, their lives were following the weekend pattern. Most jobs ended on Friday. Finish up your work for the weekend. Saturday should have been the day of rest. But it wasn't. We were desecrating it by making it the busiest day of all. She was confused. All of the answers hadn't come to her yet. She was sure there was more.

Kiz phoned an acquaintance to ask about it. What she was told was that Jesus had Risen on the first day of the week, Sunday, the Lord's Day. That's why we celebrated it as the Sabbath.

What flimsy reasoning! Deliberaately disobey because something sounded better and made more sense to our fickle, feeble human minds? That's where we always got into trouble. Kiz had no idea where to look, so she prayed for the truth.

> *"And he shall speak great words against the Most High,*
> *and shall wear out the saints of the Most High,*
> *and think to change times and laws: and they*
> *shall be given into his hand until a time and*
> *times and the dividing of time."*
> *Daniel 8:25*

Kiz knew, of course, that "he" was the devil. Times and laws will be given into his hands? God's times and laws will be given to the devil? That would explain a lot.

When she had given up most of her earthly goods, books and magazines were among the things she decided she could live without. The only book she read now was The Bible, of course, and any she felt the Lord was directing her to read. Not very many for sure, but one of those was on the table beside her bed. She opened it randomly and started to read.

She got a chill as she realized it wasn't a random opening of the book (Bible Readings for the Home Circle - Part IX "The Change of the Sabbath", page 439). She had opened it to a part of the book explaining how and why the Sabbath had been changed. And God hadn't changed it. Somewhere in the Bible, but Kiz couldn't remember where, it said (or so she thought), that whoever and whatever you obey is who or what you worship.

Apparently the early Roman Catholic Church was well aware of this and started a campaign to reverse the Sabbath from the end of the week to the beginning. They knew exactly what they were doing and by their own written accounts were pretty pleased with themselves that they were eventually successful. From what she read, she learned that they scorned the Christian Churches that followed their direction. God's Law wasn't being obeyed, their's was. Tradition. The world was blindly following the traditions of man instead of the Commandments of God.

> "...let no man go out of his place on the Seventh Day."
> In Exodus 16:29

Kiz was, in a way, relieved with what she had learned. It bothered her somewhat to "leave her place" to go to Church on Sunday. If God had said it in the Old Testament, He had His reasons. Not that she was trying to live in the Old Testament times, she wasn't. But she was trying to be obedient. She had come to the conclusion that people assumed, since Jesus had died to forgive their sins, it was okay to do whatever they wanted. They would be forgiven. It was far from the truth.

The Lord could be worshipped seven days a week, so it really didn't matter to her what day she attended Church…if she could ever find one that didn't scare the wits out of her. She would just make her preparations on Friday instead of Saturday.

"But he that knew not, and did commit things worthy
of stripes, shall be beaten with few stripes."
In Luke 12:48

Kiz heard several people in her life say that God winked at ignorance. Then they would wink. They didn't know the rest of the story apparently. After Jesus came there was no longer any excuse for ignorance.

Beating was beating. It still hurt.

She didn't feel she had much choice now in the matter. She had been told. Saturday Sabbath it was. How could she continue to disobey when God had shown her the turth? It was going to fly in the face of everything everyone believed and she would be even more nuts than she already was. But…if there was ridicule and scoffing, she would suffer it.

When the Lord took the time to show us something, Kiz believed it better be taken seriously. When the truth was revealed, we best harken. A lot more misery could be brought upon us for disobedience. And she didn't want any more of that. Saturday Sabbath it would be.

What bothered Kiz the most was how easy it was to believe a lie. The whole world, except the Jews of course, held Sunday to be the day of rest when in fact it wasn't. We were worshipping the day of the sun. She had trusted in a lie. Some other lies had already been revealed through understanding. An icy chill went through her bones as she wondered how many more lies she was still believing. How many more abominations were we committing because we believed lies?

S.S. Riley

Chapter 26

"Howbeit when He, the Spirit of truth, is come, He will
guide you into all truth: for He shall not speak of Himself;
but what so ever He shall hear, that shall He speak:
And He will shew you things to come."
John 16:13

The feelings Kiz carried that something terrible was happening began to escalate. She could sense growing apprehension mixed with a strong tinge of
fear.

Pieces that she thought to be the biggest, most important parts of the puzzle
had been coming rapid-fire over the last few months. But now, it was looking
as if it were a finely diced and chopped tossed salad. Taking all of those pieces
and fitting them back together into something recognizable felt like a daunting
task. In her weakened and deteriorated state, it was all but impossible.

She finally got on her weary knees praying half-heartedly for help. This was
not something that was just going to go away. She was well aware that she was
not in possession of anything that would be needed to do it. And doing it was
something she dreaded fully.

Crawling into her bed, Kiz knew she was defeated. Sleep. Precious sleep.
Maybe that would stop the blender that her mind had become. Forever

chipping those pieces into smaller bits that somehow, she felt, could never be pieced back together. Maybe, just maybe, it would all soon become mush. Then she could find peace and rest.

It took what seemed an eternity for her to find sleep. A voice calling her name woke her abruptly. Exactly four AM. And no one was there. Why did this have to happen? She needed rest from this torment. She was becoming exhausted.

> *"But strong meat belongeth to them that are of full age;even*
> *those who by reason of use have their senses exercised to*
> *discern both good and evil."*
> *Hebrews 5:14*

> *"...for that which is highly esteemed among men is*
> *abomination in the Sight of God."*
> *In Luke 16:15*

Groaning, Kiz went to the porch and lit a cigarette. She felt as if she was in some kind of trance or something. Scripture and understanding were coming fast and furious. She wasn't sure how long she sat there smoking, but when she finally became aware of her surroundings, the sun was coming up.

It had all finally become clear. The Lord was asking her to do something unbelievable. If she did it the way she knew it had to be done, it would be earth-shattering. The only way anyone was going to believe her was if God opened their eyes, ears, hearts and minds to accept it. She knew it was completely unacceptable in today's world.

What she needed to do was break it down into mini puzzles instead of one huge one. Figuratively, she was, to say, pick all of the carrot pieces out of her mind and reconstruct them back into a very convincing carrot. Make it believable. It sounded more reasonable to her than the nothing she had come up with. Make shorter stories instead of one very long one. It still wasn't going to be easy.

Kiz dared ask: Why me?

Because you are listening.

She shrugged and lit another cigarette. One corner of her mouth went up in a sad smile. She was about to become even more hated and unpopular than she already was.

Chapter 27

"…not to think of himself more highly than
he ought to think…"
In Romans 12:3

But man did think of himself more highly than he ought. We all did. All of the lesser idols we worshipped led up to the big one. The one we worshipped above all others: self. God included. We worshipped self over Creator. Creation worshipping creation. It couldn't be denied.

All of the little idols: life, comfort, beauty, status, convenience, position, pampering, spoiling, indulging in whatever struck our fancies, all of it meant to satiate our one true desire. All to glorify self.

Kiz didn't realize it until the early morning porch session. She should have, but apparently the Lord hadn't opened her eyes to it yet. She didn't berate herself or feel one ounce of regret about it. The time was now. Change would come.

Our worship of self led to our demands being met regardless of the consequences to others or to the world. And there were serious consequences. As long as we couldn't see it happening, it wasn't happening. But horrible things WERE happening because of it. We were just selfishly unaware is all.

Healthy, indulgent lifestyles were all the rage of the world. And Christians couldn't resist temptation. The fever had been caught. We were swept away on the world's wave of worshipping health. It was the biggest, most expensive idol, by far.

"Our Father which art in Heaven,
Hallowed be Thy Name.
Thy Kingdom come, Thy will be done
On Earth as it is in Heaven. Give us this
Day our daily bread.
And forgive us our debts, as we forgive
Our debtors. And lead us not into temptation,
But deliver us from evil:
For Thine is the Kingdom, and the Power,
And the Glory, for ever.
Amen
In Matthew 6:9-13

Nope. Nothing there about health.

When sin entered the world through Adam and Eve, we weren't abandoned by God, but we were given over to sin. Natural brute instinct. Self government. The Lord gave us specific instructions to tame that brutishness, behavior He didn't want from His creation.

But over and over and over and over again, people walked away from the Lord's way and fell back into self governing mode. Demands grew and acceptance and tolerance for evil followed. People refused to let God bring them into righteousness. Fornication, greed, lust, gluttony, envy. All of the Commands were broken. Evil was taking over.

The Lord made it clear to Kiz that we were so engrossed in self and healthcare right now that not much mention of God was made at all. Except as a supplement to healthcare.

Yes, the Lord was the Great Healer, but He was So Much More. He afflicts His people. He damns souls to eternal hellfire, He destroys whole populations and lays waste to lands that will never prosper again.

He is All. He is Everything. He is Perfect in His Ways. Kiz was awakened to the fact that we were trying to use Him for a heal me, give me, kind of God. He isn't.

Sickness and disease entered the world through sin.

It enters us for the same reason.

It is a fact of life.

> *"And He sent them to preach the Kingdom of God,*
> *and to heal the sick. And He said unto them,*
> *Take nothing for your journey..."*
> *Luke 9:2,3*

NOTHING!ABSOLUTELY NOTHING! Gee! How in the world were the disciples supposed to heal people? Don't take anything? Well...let's find out just how Jesus healed people.

> *"but speak the Word only, and my servant*
> *shall be healed,"*
> *In Matthew 8:8*

> *"Then He saith to the man..."*
> *In Matthew 12:13*

> *"For she said, If I may but touch His Clothes,*
> *I shall be made whole."*
> *Luke 5:28*

> *"And He took the damsel by the hand,*
> *and said unto her..."*
> *In Mark 5:41*

> *"Thou dumb and deaf spirit, I charge thee,*
> *come out of him..."*
> *In Mark 9:25*

"This kind can come forth by nothing,
but by prayer and fasting."
In Mark 9:29

"He said unto them…And it came to pass, that,
as they went, they were cleansed."
In Luke 17:14

"And He touched his ear and healed him."
In Luke 22:51

"Jesus saith unto him, Rise, take up
thy bed and walk."
John 5:8

Just what Kizzy thought. JESUS healed by word, touch, prayer and fasting. These were the same powers given by Him to His disciples. That's why they weren't supposed to take any cumbersome medical bags with them. They were given the POWER to heal by the One that had the power to give.

"And when He had called unto Him His twelve
disciples, He gave them Power against unclean spirits,
to cast them out, and to heal all manner of
sickness and all manner of disease."
Matthew 10:1

"And these signs shall follow them that believe;
In My Name shall they cast out devils; they shall
speak with new tongues; They shall take up serpents;
and if they drink any deadly thing, it shall
not hurt them; they shall lay hands on the
sick, and they shall recover."
Mark 16:17,18

That was really the sad part. We said we believed, but to what extent? Fairy tale belief? Real belief or lip service? The answer was obvious.

Kiz sadly recalled the young mother of four. She was diagnosed with a rare cancer and after several attempts, including a bone marrow transplant, she was found to be incurable. While speaking to a relative of the woman's, Kiz suggested laying on of hands. The reply was: "I don't think I'm qualified."

It was pretty much what Kiz expected to hear considering the relative had a doctor in the family. The world's definition of qualified is a far cry from the Lord's. Was this part of Satan's deception; was it a cultural thing or did we think Jesus would lie to us? Where did the flat-out belief that she wasn't qualified come from? All Jesus said it required was belief. The young mother passed shortly after.

Chapter 28

"...fear not..."
At least 79 times in the KJV

"...not fear..."
At least 15 times in the KJV

"I have afflicted; I will afflict..."
In Nahum 1:12

"Is any among you afflicted? Let him pray."
In James 5:13

"Is any sick among you? Let him call for the elders
of the Church, and let them pray over him, anointing him with
oil in the Name of the Lord: and the prayer of faith
shall save the sick, and the Lord shall raise
him up..."
In James 5:14,15

"Behold, we count them happy which endure."
In James 5:11

It seemed to Kizzy that when she gave herself to Christ, accepting Him as her Lord and Savior, it was ALL of her. Nothing was held back. She put herself in His Capable Hands. Body, soul, mind, heart, internal, external. It was a struggle at times to remember this, but remember she must. As she struggled, she was beginning to see that it was well worth the effort. Despite her many afflictions and the attacks on her, she could feel herself growing closer to her Lord.

She could see now that hard times were meant to keep us close or draw us back when we wandered away. She knew God would test us. Not for His Sake, but for ours. Some of these tests showed her what areas of her life she trusted Him with and what areas she needed to begin to trust or to trust more. When she thought she had put her faith, trust and hope in Him, she was shown places where she was desperately lacking.

This wasn't some kind of game we were playing. God was serious. Did we or did we not trust Him?

> *"For God so loved the world, that He gave His Only Begotten*
> *Son, that whosoever believeth in Him should not*
> *perish, but have everlasting life."*
> *John 3:16*

Kiz was awed at the story. God could have turned His Back and left us to our own evil ways. But He didn't. And He didn't just give His Son, He allowed Him to be belittled, laughed at, spit on, made fun of, beaten with lead hooks tied onto whips, tearing His Precious Flesh apart.

He was innocent of any wrong doing, yet He was lied about and forced to carry, half dead, as far as He could, His own device that was reserved for the worst of the worst. The device that would kill Him. The Cross. God didn't just give His Son, He turned Him over to evil beasts. Men.

Kiz looked at her own flesh, blood and bones, hands and feet, trying to imagine what it would feel like to have crude spikes driven through them into a piece of lumber. She knew the pain of splinters, but couldn't even come close to what Jesus had endured.

Then to be set up in the blazing sun to finish Him off. His death, His dying was beyond horrible. And God gave Him up to that. Jesus accepted, knowing full well what was going to happen.

And look at us. Jesus did not die for us so that we could continue to do whatever we wanted. He set an example. He showed and told us what was expected. We were given a complete Handbook full of Rules and Regulations, Laws and Commands. The Bible.

He told us what would happen if we obeyed, and what would happen if we didn't. It was meant to transform us, to lead us away from the behavior that condemned us in the first place. Not making that behavior okay. Why weren't we letting it happen?

> *"But if ye suffer for righteousness' sake, happy are ye:*
> *and be not afraid of their terror, neither be troubled;"*
> *1 Peter 3:14*

He is supposed to be ours, we are supposed to be His.

> *"There shall not be found among you anyone…that*
> *useth divination…"*
> *In Deuteronomy 18:10*

Kiz understood this to mean telling the future. Then she became confused. Weren't the prophets telling the future? There was probably a big difference between doing it for fun, profit and attention, and Divine Inspiration from God. From what she could recall, the prophets didn't really want to do it. Look at Jonah. Regardless, if she pondered on this too long, it would become a distraction from what the Spirit had told her to do. That couldn't happen, it had to get done.

So…it was given to Kiz that we shouldn't be handing our bodies over to medical authorities for testing. If we weren't to know the future, why did we go seeking after it? Wasn't that just another form of astrology? Only using different methods? If we had given ourselves to Jesus, what right did we have to then turn around and give ourselves to doctors? Did that then mean we had two masters and not one? We weren't to uncover our naked-ness, so why did we?

We gave our Christ-owned bodies over to science to be tested and treated, ex-perimented on and healed, probed and poked, examined and checked by mere men who claimed to have what? Extensive WORLDLY learning and knowl-edge? THEY were QUALIFIED? By who? By God? No, by the world.

> *"...for that which is highly esteemed among men is*
> *abomination in the Sight of God."*
> *In Luke 16:15*

What were the three most highly esteemed idols in the world today besides self? Kiz's skin crawled. Medicine, education and technology. Hmm...that meant they must be abominations. But who would believe that?

The body was designed by God to heal itself. It did the job nicely. Doctors even claimed that about 95% of illnesses that people come to them for would be gone in 3 to 5 days if left alone. The only reason those doctors gave us pre-scription drugs was that we demanded we be healed. We refuse to be afflicted by anything.

Why?

Were we afraid to be sick? Maybe it didn't fit into OUR conception of ideal. Did we think that what we were doing was so important we couldn't be in-convenienced? Did we demand that WE be in control and not God? Or was it because the WORLD told us that if we were sick we weren't healthy and THAT was unacceptable? Health was, of course, the biggest idol concerning our idol selves and we had to serve that health idol no matter what.

We wouldn't even suffer a slight headache or the teensiest bit of a runny nose. It had to be treated. It had to be stopped and it had to be stopped now. Our health demanded it.

If God wanted us to be healed and healthy, didn't we think He could do it?

S.S. Riley

Well, we never really gave Him a chance now, did we? We ran to the doctor at the first sign of anything. Doctors were highly esteemed. But was the Lord?

"And it is appointed unto men once to die..."
In Hebrews 9:27

If our body and God didn't heal us, could it just be our time to die? If it was our time to go, but we demanded that medical science save us, were we missing the boat?

Again, what were we so afraid of? That God wasn't strong enough to take care of those we left behind? Was our ego so big we believed the world couldn't go on without us? Was it the big health idol the world was pushing down our throats? Fear of death? That should be for the lost world, not for believers. Why did we feel we had to be saved when Jesus had already done that for us? Why did we require physical healing when we knew all that mattered was the Spiritual kind?

Kiz had once heard a preacher on the Christian radio station say it was our job to keep people alive as long as we could. She didn't even look for it in the Bible because she knew it wasn't there. We were on the wide path, entering in at the wide gate. Why couldn't we see that?

*"And said, If thou wilt diligently hearken to the Voice of
the Lord thy God, and wilt do that which is right
in His Sight, and wilt give ear to His Commandments,
and keep all His Statutes, I will put none of these
diseases upon you...for I am the Lord that healeth thee."*
In Exodus 15:26

Kiz wondered if illness and disease were tests or punishments. Probably both.

*"Thinkest thou that I cannot now pray to My Father, and He
shall presently give Me more than twelve legions of angels?
But how then shall the Scriptures be fulfilled, that
thus it must be?"*
Matthew 26:53,54

Considering Jesus was fully human and fully God, why didn't He let the human part override the Will of God like we do? He could have. Why didn't He? Was it because He knew that God's Will was of Supreme Importance? That God was wise and we weren't?

Where it was said that Jesus knew and experienced all of our temptations, Kiz felt a new lightening. The temptation to disobey must have been strong, just as it is in us. Did we possess the same strength that the human part of Jesus had, but neglected to tap into it? Could that be a love so strong for our Creator that we didn't want to disobey? That we are one with Jesus and with God and that our disobedience directly involves them too?

Kiz decided that Jesus was showing by example again. Complete trust. No matter what happens. God knows best no matter how it looks to the world.

Kiz believed nothing could happen to us unless God allowed it to happen. And it always happened for a reason. Why then fight personal affliction? If it was the Will of God, how could we fight it anyway? Tooth and nail? Any means available, even if it does involve evil?

The sin doesn't lie in the affliction. It lies in how we approach that affliction.

Would the Good Lord come through with a miracle cure so the credit could be given to man? So the glory could go to men? He is a jealous God, remember?

*"Why criest thou for thine affliction? Thy sorrow is
incurable for the multitude of thine iniquity: because thy sins
were increased, I have done these things unto thee."
Jeremiah 30:15*

*"Is there no balm in Gilead?; is there no physician
there? Why then is not the health of the daughter of
My people recovered?"
Jeremiah 8:22*

We are blind to our iniquities. We cannot see them. Pray for the Lord to open our eyes.

"For when they shall say, Peace and safety; then
sudden destruction cometh upon them…"
In 1 Thessalonians 5:3

The Lord had shown Kiz that there was no peace or safety and there wouldn't be until Jesus came to reign. Statistics were proving it. The news was proving it. Lists of bad drugs were growing every day and screamed it. But people weren't listening. The enemy was striking us from within. Not within our own country, but within our own bodies. And we were eagerly assisting.

"For whosoever will save his life shall lose it…"
In Matthew 6:25

Kiz read this passage over and over. How many times had she saved her life? Had she lost her eternal life? Hmm…

We were afraid of everything except what we were supposed to be afraid of.

"But I will forwarn you Whom ye shall fear: Fear Him,
which after He hath killed hath Power to cast
into hell; yea, I say unto you, Fear Him."
Luke 12:5

It seemed to her that we, referring to ourselves as believers, sure didn't believe the right things. Why was that?

"And Asa in the thirty and ninth year of his reign
was diseased in his feet, until his disease was
exceeding great: yet in his disease he sought not to the
Lord, but to physicians…and died…"
In 2 Chronicles 16:12,13

Yes, Kiz knew the Bible had a great deal to teach us, but there wasn't much time for that kind of learning, was there?

She decided it was time, once and for all: did she trust the All Powerful Creator with her life, or not?

The decision couldn't be no.

The livelihood of the world preyed on scaring us. It couldn't afford not to. It wanted too much stuff. Fear was one of Satan's tricks. If we truly trusted God, what did we have to fear?

Yikes! We didn't fully trust did we? Is that why we were so afraid?

So we let the world scare us, causing us to live lives we shouldn't be living, meddling in things we should be fleeing from and we were paying dearly because of it. Putting our trust where it shouldn't be, then wondering why all these awful things were happening to us.

Her natural tendency was to fear what was going to become of her in the world because of what the Lord had asked her to do. Then again, she wondered what would happen to her if she didn't do it. One carried more serious consequences than the other. The choice was made.

During the chain-smoking porch session, God had shown her that healthcare was of the beast. It was the most evil, wicked, dangerous, expensive idol we bowed to. We were dealing with people who were wolves in sheep's clothing and didn't even know it. Somewhere along the way, Satan had kicked the compassion-of-healthcare door wide open and it had become twisted. People had to be told.

Now she needed to begin making her case.

S.S. Riley

Chapter 29

"Neither repented they of their murders, nor of their
sorceries, nor of their fornication, nor of
their thefts."
Revelation 9:21

"for thy merchants were the great men of the earth;
for by thy sorceries were all nations deceived."
In Revelation 18:23

Kiz searched her memory. If it was serving her correctly, most of the Bible was written in three languages. Greek, Hebrew and Aramaic. She seemed to recall there were a few more in which smaller parts were written. It didn't matter, there wasn't time for that now. More distraction from her purpose. Greek was there for sure.

Her input of information started long before the day she heard a sermon preached by a well-known pastor on her car radio. He explained that sorcery translated into Greek was pharmakon. And it meant drug. That's all. One word. Drug. Her line of thinking was that in English pharmakon would translate back into sorcery. But it didn't seem to work that way. Pharmakon translated into English is, are you ready? Pharmacy. Pharmakon equals pharmacy. It seemed that sorcery boiled down to drugs. Drug. Drugstore. Druggists.

The preacher went on to explain that, oh, no, it didn't mean legal prescription drugs, it was referring to illegal street drugs.

Her mind screamed WHAT? ARE YOU BLIND? She knew better.

Kiz had long had bad feelings about doctors and medicine. Kind of like two magnets repelling each other. Her dread of the whole thing, it appeared to her now, was probably founded and grounded in a vague discernment. Truly, this information came as no surprise to her.

She could not, however, agree with the messenger. If what he said was so, why then was sorcery in the same category as pharmacy? Why did it not translate into illegal street drugs? Again, Kiz believed Jesus and our Creator did not use words haphazardly in the Manual. The Bible said exactly what it was meant to say. Read those two verses from Revelation at the beginning of the chapter again. Is it possible that sorcery is black magic, magic potions and cures for all of your ills? Drugs?

The preacher had to be blinded to the truth. He was misleading people. Was he making excuses and allowances for himself? Kiz wondered how many drugs he was taking that he was afraid to give up. Or refused to give up. Why hadn't he picked another topic?

Magic. Kiz had always heard that any kind of magic carried it's own consequences. Usually bad. She NEVER prayed for anything "no matter what it takes." She wasn't that selfish. She could be bringing untold suffering on herself, someone or something else. Magic potions somehow didn't fit anywhere in what she imagined a Christian would or should be. Not by anything she had read in the Bible anyway.

She tried to do her own research to find out whether these things were so. She was past believing what people told her. Pastors included. She was no longer going to accept anything, unquestioned, that carried even a hint of doubt, didn't feel right or was important. This was important.

She didn't have a computer so she looked in Webster's. Sorcery had a Latin origin. Sors, lot or chance. It meant to be under evil influence. She had no way of translating sorcery into Greek, so she called the library, gave them the facts and asked if it was true. She was told yes, it was.

The basic equation was true as far as she could prove it.

Sorcery = pharmakon = pharmacy = drug.

Roll that ball around in your head for awhile and see what you come up with.

Satan threw that right up in her face! Hypocrite! Fake! What right do you have to criticize?

She had used sorcery in her life, but hadn't realized what it was. Like the time she was bleeding to death. Passing blood clots the size of slices of beef liver. When she first called her doctor to ask about excessive bleeding, the doctor said, oh, the fibroid tumors.

What? Fibroid tumors? You never told me about fibroid tumors. "Well…we didn't need to say anything unless you started having problems."

The doctor prescribed birth control pills. Two a day ought to do the trick. It didn't work. Each time Kiz called, the dose increased. Three, four, then five a day. They should, over time, shrink the tumors and stop the bleeding. They didn't. Kiz was running out of time. The bleeding was worse than ever. Kiz was so weak she could barely get out of a chair. The doctor never suggested coming in for an appointment.

Kiz's mother did make an appointment, with a different doctor. He sent her straight to the emergency room. He cancelled the rest of his appointments for the day and performed an emergency hysterectomy. His suggestion was to sue the first doctor for malpractice. Oh, no, Kiz couldn't do that, she just wanted to get better.

She had a sneaking suspicion the second doctor pursued something because she found out later the first doctor had shut down her practice.

Then there was the car wreck where she spent three months in the burn unit at the local children's hospital. Lots of sorcery and magic going on in there.

Apparently Kiz hadn't lived beyond what she was supposed to live because the Lord was using her. Unless…she had been deceived to believe the Lord was using her. She would find out when she finally did die, wouldn't she?

It had been, what now, five or six years since she made her own personal choice never to seek medical attention again? That was one point where she definitely trusted the Lord. He would take her when it was His time.

And she was looking forward to it. Death was the ONLY vehicle that could take us to our eternal home. She was sure sick and tired of this one. Yes. As her own personal choice, Kiz's days of worshipping health and healthcare were over. And she was done thinking of herself as a hypocrite. Repenting, in her mind, was a lifelong process. You didn't know it was wrong until it was proven to you that it was.

> *"take heed, regard not iniquity: for this hast thou*
> *chosen rather than affliction."*
> *KJV Job 36:21*

This was a little cloudy in Kizzy's mind, but she was determined to clear it up. It could easily have been overlooked by a hasty reading, but she wasn't into hasty readings anymore. The Spirit laid it on her heart to check it out further.

> *"Beware of turning to evil, which you seem to prefer*
> *to affliction."*
> *NIV Job 36:21*

It sounded somewhat clearer in the NIV, but needed to be dissected.

Beware: danger! Look out!

Evil was evil, but how could it be recognized by a blinded, happy-go-lucky soul that had been taught everything was okay? One that accepted everything?

Affliction was pain, suffering, any cause of suffering. (Webster's)

Affliction would include illness, sickness and disease.

S.S. Riley

Obviously we like evil better than we like affliction.

Most of the time the Bible doesn't tell us why. Just do it or don't do it. As when you tell a little kid not to stick his hand in the fire, but he does it anyway. Maybe that's why we aren't given a reason. It doesn't matter. God knows we're going to do it regardless.

And why was it we paid so much attention to every single physical symptom in our body? Every ache and pain, discomfort and odd color, but didn't recognize symptoms of spiritual illness? We were always trying to find physical reasons for them, passing them off as imbalances or lack of this or too much of that. Making it into a physical, bodily problem that we then demanded be treated with pills. If we didn't like the way we felt, we looked into a pill bottle for change.

Look to the plastic bottle instead of the Maker. We were depending on our own and the world's wiles for healing.

And we were failing miserably.

The United States of America is one of the top sickliest countries in the world despite having "the best health care system" in the world. Ever wonder why? Ever hear that "the cure is worse than the disease?" It's true. Our cures are killing us.

Kiz hadn't read magazines for quite a long while, but someone had given her some. They were in her car. She planned to give them to the homeless shelter to help people pass the time. She needed proof of what she knew, so she retrieved one of the women's magazines from her car and took a peek.

The first drug she came to was for a vaginal lubricant. Make your fornication and adultery more pleasant and fulfilling. She started reading for side effects. There were plenty.

unusual vaginal bleeding	heart attack
blood clots	stroke
breast cancer	dimentia

uterine cancer
ovarian cancer
liver problems
severe headaches
fluid retention
nausea
yeast infection
enlargement of benign tumors
changes in speech or vision
swollen lips, face, tongue
severe pain in chest or legs with or
without shortness of breath,
weakness and fatigue

high blood pressure
high blood sugar
breast lumps
vomiting
breast pain
hair loss
gall bladder disease
severe allergic reaction
burning, irritation, itching
abdominal cramps, bloating

(as stated in : "Family Circle, August 2015)

It said absolutely nothing about adverse side effects in men, but Kiz was sure there had to be some. Poor, unsuspecting guy, thinks he's just going to get a little. Little does he know. It's fake, it's a lie, it's dangerous. But nobody cares. Let's have us some sin!

The next one she came to was for arthritis. The ad clearly stated right on the front page that movement and exercise were the best remedy. But, who wants to do that when we can just pop a pill?

Try these! Feel better now!
Danger! Beware! Lookout!
Suffer more later.
Only a few side effects on this one.

more likely to get infections
makes infections worse
increased cancer risk
unusual cancers
cough that does not go away
hepatitis B
heart failure

lymphoma
basal cell cancer
TB
high fever
weight loss
liver problems
rash

S.S. Riley

nervous system problems	blood problems
upper respiratory infection	psoriasis
allergic reactions	headaches
immune disorders	nausea

squamous cell cancer of the skin
wasting (loss of fat and muscle tissue)
rare cancer called "hepotosphenic T cell lymphoma - often deadly, mostly in young men

(as stated in: "Family Circle", August 2015)

She was getting her proof.

The third ad for a prescription drug was an anti-depressent. Sounded like these were just the ticket.

right upper belly pain	itching
yellow skin and eyes	dark urine
stiff muscles	confusion
serious or peeling rash	skin blisters
mouth sores	hives
problems with urine flow	dizziness
inability to concentrate	weakness
high fever	unsteadiness
unusual changes in behavior	falls
unexplained flu-like symptoms	headache

liver problems - severe, sometimes fatal

(as stated in: "Family Circle, December 2012)

That was enough. It was only the first three, but Kiz didn't need to see any more. Satan's hand was definitely in the mix.

Wake up people! What was being drilled into our heads as being good, wasn't. It was bad. Really, really bad. The magazine went back into her car.

Could the benefits really outweigh the risks? She wasn't so sure about that.

We had been brainwashed. We DEMANDED that we be healed and drug companies were working to fill that demand. We were listening to the world, but we weren't listening to God. There didn't seem to be any common sense left in the world. What had happened to us?

Kiz sadly shook her head as she thought about a dear, sweet friend. They had discussed the dangers of her meds, she knew what would probably happen. She apparently didn't care. Her response? "I follow those directions to the letter."

A lot of good that was going to do. Well over 100,000 people die every year from taking their prescription drugs EXACTLY as directed. The drugs we so trusted were killing us.

Kiz didn't ask her friend if she followed God's Directions to the letter. She already knew the answer.

So…if over 100,000 people die every year because they trusted their doctors, there were many times that number of people who are suffering from serious, debilitating, soon-to-be deadly side effects.

Permanent side effects that require more drugs with more side effects.

We are led to believe we wouldn't or couldn't live without drugs. We are losing our lives, dropping like flies because of it. Are we losing our eternal lives by depending on this kind of evil to save us and make our miserable lives more comfortable? Or are we just paying the price for it here on earth?

It all starts in infancy. Our children are supposed to be a blessing from God. But Satan probably hates that as much as he hates everything else. Why not mutilate that blessing?

The first day of a helpless infant's life, it is given a shot. Kiz couldn't recall if it was against hepatitis or tetanus, but it was one of those, maybe meningitis. Yes, at birth, we start pumping our children full of the same toxic substances we were pumping into ourselves. Those first shots probably have the same side effects as what we adults were poisoning ourselves with.

All in the name of health and safety. We were damaging our children beyond repair. We weren't chasing after God or Jesus, we were chasing after the beast and he wanted to keep it that way. Sick children, if they survived, grew into sick adults, all demanding cures. In our quest to fix everything we saw as a problem, we were creating myriads more.

When it came to the kind of money involved in an illusive cure, corruption invaded every level of life. From the thief that sold on the streets to the highest level of politics. People were all the same, some just had higher positions. Many more were involved than not involved. Politicians and government officials were bought and sold. High level employees moved back and forth between government jobs and drug company positions. And they all had agendas, all paving the way for more toxic drugs and less preessure to stop selling them.

There were billions of dollars in profit every year, providing huge payoffs and bribes. Almost all elected officials owned shares in these businesses. They expected profits, not losses. They worked toward that very end. More money.

They preyed on gullible people. There must be a lot of them to have billions in proft in one year. There was criminal activity and complete disregard for human life involved. All because of money.

They didn't care. They had no conscience. As long as the money rolled in, the sorcery rolled out.

Death by prescriptiion drug is the 4th largest cause of death in the United States. It would probably move to No. 1 if the three ahead of it could be proven to be attributed to drugs. The three ahead of it include cancer and heart attack.

We were willing victims. Were we victims of murder? If they knew it caused death, but sold it anyway, wasn't it murder? Or should it be considered suicide? If you knew the risks, but did it anyway, what should it be called?

When Syria used chemical weapons to kill people, Kiz could only see high level hypocrites flapping their jaws, acting all indignant. We were allowing a very silent, very deadly chemical attack on the American people every second of every single day. When we get THAT beam out of our own eye, then we can start picking at the speck in Syria's.

True to form, when, with the Spirit's help, Kiz finally got a piece of the huge puzzle fitted together, her attempt was fortified. While at her son's house he turned on a documentary released in 2013 called "American Addict." He was big on documentaries. It spurred her with the urgent need to get this done. She recommended the documentary strongly to everyone. "Please, find it and watch it. It won't be a waste of time. American Addict."

Kiz was well aware that nothing could, or rather would, be done to stop anything. All she could do was step away and let the world go on being Satan's domain. She wanted very badly to step away.

Chapter 30

"And the swine…he is unclean to you."
In Leviticus 11:7

So the tables have turned.

What's that supposed to mean? I've been to see you many times. Not even a hello?

Yes, hello Paul.

You've been to see me many times, but not with that look on your face. Is that how I appear to you?

If I knew how I looked, I might be able to answer that question.

Have a seat before you fall over.

That bad, huh?

Surely. What's up?

Do you remember Kate?

I know several Kates, so, yes, I probably do.

Not now, this is too important for sarcasm.

Sorry. Which Kate?

The one that came to the church for about two years. Worked at City Hospital.

Oh, yes, Kate. Why did she leave?

My gut instinct says Kelly, but Kate said she went back to Iowa to take care of ailing parents.

Yes, it is all about Kelly, isn't it?

She thinks so, quite the ego.

So why bring up Kate if she's in Iowa?

Well, she came back for a quick family visit here. I saw her at the airport when she was on her way back home.

To Iowa?

Yes, she lives there now. Married a farmer.

Thought she would have married a doctor.

She probably would have.

If?

That's part of the story. Her plane was delayed and she was just sitting there waiting. So I asked her to dinner.

I take it she went.

S.S. Riley

I wouldn't let her refuse.

Oh no. It didn't turn into some kind of affair, did it? Is that why you look so terrified?

You know me better than that. No. There was no affair. It's what she told me at dinner.

Which is?

She said she'd heard rumors at City, but never personally saw anything to back them up. Then she got a job at another hospital after her move. And the evidence was right there in front of her. She couldn't deny it any longer. She had to start on night shift because that was where the only openings were. She only stayed a week and quit.

I'll bet they were glad they hired her.

She said the Lord convicted her and she couldn't be involved any longer. The idea of marrying a doctor made her want to vomit.

Interesting. And?

Pigs, darn it, pigs.

Go on.

She said that truckloads of live pigs were delivered to the hospital under deep, dark cover of the night.

And she thought they should parade them in with fanfare through the front door at noon for everyone to see? Confetti and streamers and little party whistles? That would be real sanitary.

You aren't understanding this.

Oh, I understand completely. My grandson was born with a cataract. The doctors told my daughter the only way that could happen was if the mother had been taking steroids. They treated her rather shabbily.

Was she?

Not to her knowledge. She told them she was Army and they would have to check those records.

So the Government gives people steroids without permission or telling anyone they're doing it?

Couldn't say for sure. Probably so.

Sorry to hear that, but what's it got to do with what we were talking about?

When they were scheduling surgery for the boy, they told her and her husband they had two choices. They could replace parts of his eye with parts from a pig's eye, or they could choose for him to wear a contact or glasses.

I'm feeling ill.

Don't. They refused the pig eye. Contacts didn't work. The boy is virtually blind in his left eye.

Does she have regrets?

No. And ironically, the military won't be able to take him because of it. He wants to be Air Force.

Lawsuit?

Yea, right.

Oh, now that you mention it…

They've been using pigs to patch people up for decades.

I know, but…

Where did you, or she for that matter, think they got pig parts? Out of thin air?

No. I don't know. It's like one of those things you're so used to hearing that you're dull to it. You don't pay any attention to it. Like hunger in Africa. If it isn't right in front of you, you can't see how bad it really is.

Until the Lord throws it right into your face. Then it gets up close and personal.

Yeah. Exactly.

I take it there's more.

Much, much more.

Whenever you're ready.

I had a vision. I think. If it wasn't a vision, it was the worst nightmare I've ever had. But I don't think I was asleep and I usually don't remember my dreams. It seemed so real. So disgustingly real.

And terrifying?

Yes. I was watching as some people in long white coats and face masks carried a squealing pig to a stainless steel table. One of them prepared a syringe while the others fought to hold the pig on it's side. A man held the hypodermic up and pushed the air out of it. I could see a drop of something glistening on the end of the needle. He made some kind of joke and everyone laughed. Then he gave the pig a shot in the leg. It squealed louder and fought harder. Then it gradually stopped moving and lay still.

Nothing. Silence.

They started putting it on some sort of life support. Tubes and machines and an IV. Then they shaved off it's hair and scrubbed it with some orange stuff. They rinsed it off with a shower of water and a man stepped up with a scalpel. He started cutting. The pig was alive and he was dissecting it.

The fresher the better.

People were lined up with silver platters. A part of the pig would go onto a platter. The person holding it would set the platter on the floor, bow down to it, then pick up the pig piece and kiss it. Then they would leave. The next person would step up to get their pig piece and do the same ritual. They had blood on their hands and faces, but when they smiled their teeth were white and glistening. Like that fake sparkle that shows how clean your mouth is. There was soft, soothing, relaxing music playing like that was going to make it all better. As each person ran out of the room, a lady with a clipboard would yell out a name and number.

Patients.

When the last person in line took their piece of pig and started to worship it, the doors burst open and people wearing chef's hats ran in. They ripped out the tubes and put what was left of the pig in a big soup pot. Then they danced out of the room like a conga line.

That's it?

Isn't that enough?

What do you want me to say?

Maybe that we're evil and demented, insane and perverted, a sick society that God has every right to wipe off the face of the planet?

I agree 100%. But, we worship our lives.

And you never talked to me about this?

It never came up.

But, now it did.

Apparently. We're talking.

Lord Jesus help us all. What are we thinking? What is wrong with us? What are we doing?

We're blinded.

To that extent? Where we think it's perfectly alright to save our own worthless hides by sacrificing some poor animal in a satanic ritual? Using them to replace parts that shouldn't even be replaced? Jesus died for this? I don't believe it. How can we stop it? It has to be stopped.

We can't stop it any more than we can stop any other horrific behavior like vaccinations and genetically altered foods. We're living in Satan's territory and his main goal is to destroy all of God's Perfect Creation.

He's doing a pretty good job of it.

Yes, he is, on this plane anyway. There is a lot he can't touch and a lot we can't see. God really is in control.

I know. But how could anyone even consider having pig parts put into them. I mean...seriously, think about it. Do we really believe God wants us to be doing this kind of stuff?

Do you remember the lady that came to the Church wanting to be baptized by immersion?

Yeah. I do. Everyone thought she was so odd. Never been to the Church before and didn't want to be a member, just wanted to be baptized the proper way.

In her mind it was the ONLY way.

Did she ever say why?

Yes. Jim asked me to talk to her before he baptized her. She said that baptize means immerse. She said that the weavers and dyers of cloth baptized what they made to make it different, a different piece. To bring new life into it. It couldn't be sprinkled, it had to be put completely and totally into the dye to be baptized properly. Who wanted a piece of linen with a few drops of purple or blue on it? You can't clean dishes or laundry by sprinkling water on them. I understood that, but didn't understand why she didn't believe sprinkling was true baptism.

Did she explain?

Kind of. She said the old man has to be buried with Christ and we can't be born again of water if we aren't in it. She said sprinkling was a symbol of baptism, but not the real thing. We had to follow Jesus' example, then repeated that baptize means immerse.

Why didn't she get baptized at her own Church?

She said she tried, but the preacher got mad. He told her she didn't have any respect for their traditions and was making problems where there shouldn't be any. She said he even mentioned someone belittling his beliefs during the next sermon.

Did you invite her to come to our Church?

Yeah. She said the Lord had her where she was for a reason.

Jim baptized her though, didn't he?

Yes, he most certainly did. Then he baptized me, my wife and all of the kids and grandkids. We had been sprinkled at our last Church back in Cincy, but she was very convincing. And we didn't want to take any chances.

All well and good, but what's the connection here?

Oh, that. She said that 35 years earlier she had been riding in a car that was hit by a semi. The diesel fuel caught on fire and she was trapped in the car, burning alive.

Ouch.

She said that when she was in the hospital undergoing procedure after procedure, someone came in and gave her a shot of what they called a twilight drug. I think she used the name Ketamine, but I'm not sure. It made her mentally alert on certain levels, but separated completely from her body. She said it was extremely unsettling, like part of her was detached and watching.

Some magic potion, huh?

Most certainly. She said that after that a smiling woman approached her telling her that they would try to use as much of her own skin for grafts as possible. But if there wasn't enough, they would use pig skin.

They attack you when you can't defend yourself.

Exactly. She said she heard the words, but they meant nothing to her at the time. There was no thought to accept or reject. She really had no idea what was going on.

So why was she telling you this?

Because when she was finally alert from the surgery, she remembered. It always bothered her and she didn't know whether the Lord would forgive her or not, whether it would do any good to be baptized in the first place. She couldn't see any righteousness in it. She told me that if she knew which was the pig skin she would gladly cut it off and suffer the consequences.

Maybe there was enough of her own skin.

Maybe not.

What did you say to her?

Nothing. I didn't know what to say and I didn't want to tell her a lie because I really don't know. That woman was suffering thirty-five years later because of a choice she couldn't make. Satan is relentless in his attacks on helpless, innocent people.

You didn't tell her that?

You know how it is. The answers, smart remarks and retorts don't come until after the fact. Two hours later you think, yeah, well, I should've said this or that.

Too late.

Maybe for good reason, huh?

I s'pose.

Listen, I have to go. Thanks. Nothing is any better, it's all as wrong as anything can be, but at least I got it off my chest for now.

No problem. We can talk more later.

Don't know that it will do any good, but thanks.

I don't know either.

'Bye for now.

'Bye. And hey, don't be eating any pork in the hospital cafeteria.

Yuck. Thanks for the advice.

"That ye abstain from meats offered to idols…"
In Acts 15:29

Chapter 31

*"He that toucheth the dead body of any man shall be
unclean for seven days."*
Numbers 19:11

*"And whosoever toucheth one that is slain with a sword
in the open fields, or a dead body, or a bone
of a man, or a grave, shall be unclean
seven days."*
Numbers 19:16

*"Then said Haggai, If one that is unclean by a dead
body touch any of these, shall it be
unclean? And the priests answered and said,
It shall be unclean."*
Haggai 2:13

*"Ye are the children of the Lord your God: ye shall
not cut yourselves,...for the dead."*
In Deuteronomy 14:1

"Thou shalt not suffer a witch to live."
Exodus 22:18 KJV

"Do not allow a sorceress to live."
Exodus 22:18 NIV

There were many aspects of the world Kiz could just say no to. Other parts weren't that easy. She felt trapped, forced to live by standards she didn't really want to abide by. One of those was her car. Financial affairs refused to allow her to be where she wanted to be, living the way the Lord had laid on her heart to live. She couldn't very well just go be a squatter somewhere. So she was stuck with the car.

It was her birthday month. Her license and plates both needed to be renewed. She got her number at the BMV and took a seat to wait. That's when another chunk of the puzzle came crashing into place. She was seriously thinking about walking away from the whole mess, when a woman behind the counter asked another customer if they were an organ donor. "Yes."

The Light came on high beam. Warning! Warning!

God does not change, His Word does not change. Nor will it ever. Nowhere in the Old Testament or in the New Testament could Kiz ever remember that the status of a dead body had changed from unclean to clean. God knows everything. He was bound to know that advanced medical science would some-day start delving into the unnatural. Digging around in a corpse for usable parts. The sinisterness of it struck her like a Mack truck. It looked like evil beyond your normal evil. Evil pushing itself to the limit.

How desperate the world must be to hang on to life. Why did we think we had to fix every single physical problem? There seemed to be no extent we wouldn't go to save our lives. Just because the world could, and did, didn't make it right.

We could watch porn, but was it right for a Christian? We could be dishonest, but where was the righteousness in that? Didn't God's Word tell us that just because we could didn't mean we were supposed to? There were a great many things we weren't supposed to do. Still, there seemed to be no stopping point where our idol, healthcare, was concerned. Hooray for healthcare! Gotta have healthcare! Did we have any idea where we were going and what we were doing for this idol?

Wasn't it a known fact that the body rejected foreign objects? Yes, it was. So it would reject an organ put into it from a dead body. And it does. But wait! Hold on! The world had developed anti-rejection drugs to make their efforts successful. Yippee! Now the body God had created could be forced to comply with the wishes of worldly experimenters. Yes, the world was working diligently to override every mechanism the Good Lord had put in place.

A vision flitted through Kiz's mind and at that instant she knew how real sorcery was. It was being applied to every area of our lives and stemmed from scientific and medical experiments. Her vision was not of witches in black hats and capes mixing up magic potions in boiling cauldrons. There were no frog legs and toad warts and bat wings. What she saw were men and women in long white coats mixing their magic potions with elaborate machines and test tubes. Using pieces and parts from aborted fetuses, monkeys, pigs and cows

She was literally frozen by the comparison. How could it be denied? What difference was there? None that she could see. And it put many things under a new light. How had we come to believe that deviant behavior like this was the Will of God?

Between the time she had picked up her number and sat down, until now, still waiting, the Lord had opened her eyes to the fact that our mental state was far, far worse than our physical state could ever be. Believing lies was a form of cancer in our brains, making us mentally ill in a way we could never comprehend.

Kiz wanted to crawl into a hole or under a rock and never come out again. The implications of all of this was mind boggling. Whoever said truth was stranger than fiction must have had some whoppers of experiences. She knew how they felt.

If sorcery boiled down to drugs, and it did, what did that make the people who were involved in them from beginning to end? Kiz cringed. She couldn't say the words. But she knew she had to: sorcerers? sorceresses?

We were all up to our ears in sorcery. And we didn't even bother to find out what we were involved in. Jobs in the medical field were one of the most highly esteemed careers there are. One of the three fastest growing businesses in the world. It's where the best paying jobs are. Who was going to believe something like this?

Kiz half smiled as she realized that when this all came out, she was going to be one of the most hated people of all time. Vaguely, in the back of her mind she wondered again, "Why me?"

She listened to the cheerful idle chitchat all around her and somehow longed to fit in. She didn't. No reason to even try. It would be a lie. This sort of chatter just to fill the time had become inane to her. She decided she really must be crazy.

It didn't matter somehow. She knew the Spirit was taking her on a one-way journey. There would be no coming back. Where He would take her, only He knew.

Kizzy answered "absolutely not" to the organ donor question, got her new license and stickers and trudged through the snow to the car she didn't really want. It was just another anchor to the world she wasn't supposed to be a part of.

Chapter 32

"Now the serpent was more subtil than any beast of the field which the Lord God had made."
In Genesis 3:1

"And the woman said,
The serpent beguiled me,
and I did eat."
In Genesis 3:13

There was an ambulance in front of Kiz. Not with lights flashing and sirens blaring, it was just rolling along. When it stopped at a red light with Kiz's car behind it, something seemed to glow on the back of it. Of course Kiz looked. She wasn't really nosy, she just noticed things.

In the dim, pulsing light, she saw two snakes wrapped around what looked like a walking stick. Two snakes. The symbol that the field of medicine used. She remembered that it was the ancient symbol used by some supposed god of healing. Why did they still use that particular emblem? The answer was obvious. Satan was at work.

The snake was a symbol of evil. Didn't we know that? Surely we did. And why two snakes? Wasn't one bad enough? Did it mean double trouble? The beast AND the false prophet? How in the world could we believe that something symbolized by two snakes would be good? Did we even bother to look? No. We just believed it.

All of a sudden a grim determination seized her. The world had to be told. She would be hated by many people, probably all of them, but they and their souls mattered too much to her. There was no way that two snakes could represent something good from the Holy Trinity. She must present these facts and pray that God would open minds and eyes.

"Go ye into all the world, and preach the Gospel to every creature."
Mark 16:15

Kiz may have been wrong, but nowhere in the Great Commission could she discern anything about being told to go heal, only preach the Gospel.

"And He ordained TWELVE, that they should be with Him,
and that He might send them forth to preach. And
to have Power to heal sickness, and to cast out devils."
Mark 3:14,15
(emphasis mine)

"and when He had called unto Him His TWELVE disciples,
he gave them Power against unclean spirits, to cast them
out, and to heal all manner of sickness and all
manner of disease."
Matthew 10:1
(emphasis mine)

Here, only Jesus Himself and his twelve disciples had this special Power. Kiz knew that in the 10th chapter of Luke, Jesus also gave this Power to 70 other men. But it came with restrictions. They weren't to speak to anyone while on their journey. If a city believed their message and let them stay, they were to heal there. If a city did not believe their message, they were to brush the dust off their feet, basically curse that city, and go on their way.

The only other instance she could think of was the disciples complaining to Jesus that ONE who was not with their party was casting out demons. They had told him to stop, but Jesus said let him be. The narrative said nothing about the man healing sickness and disease, he was casting out demons.

The Power had only been given to a total of 82 men on two total occasions. That included Judas. Kiz didn't bother to look and find out if the man who replaced Judas was given this Power. If he was, the total would have been 83. They didn't take along any big, black bags full of magic tricks. Jesus had given them the POWER to heal.

> "For nation shall rise against nation, and kingdom
> against kingdom: and there shall be famines, and pestilences,
> and earthquakes in divers places."
> Matthew 24:7

Jesus was giving advance warning, signs of things to come. They weren't marching orders. There would be calamity, there would be sickness and disease. Some pieces of the puzzle seemed much harder to put into place. Kiz was struggling again. She got on her knees. "Father God, if You want me to understand, please shine the Light. If not, please just let me live a peaceful life and let all of this stuff go away."

Contrary to her own personal wishes, the Light started to shine.

> "For such are false apostles, deceitful workers, transforming
> themselves into the apostles of Christ. And no
> marvel; for Satan himself is transformed into an angel of
> light. Therefore it is no great thing if his ministers also be
> transformed as the ministers of righteousness;
> whose end shall be according to their works."
> 2 Corinthians 11:13-15

> "For false christs and prophets shall rise, and shall
> shew signs and wonders…"
> In Mark 13:22

We were told by Jesus to go and preach the Gospel. Kiz didn't recall that we were ever commissioned to participate in any war on disease. Did we just assume such a thing or was there something she had missed? She kept up her search of the Bible for quite some time and could find nothing along those lines.

As far as she could see, when we went to preach the Gospel, we were taking satan's big bag of deceptive tricks with us. That bag contained sorcery, magic potions and black magic.

When we went on relief missions in disaster stricken areas, we took food, clothing and medicine. The Gospel took a backseat. It was supposed to be first and foremost. "We bring you healing in the Name of Jesus!" What were we telling people?

Were people turning to Christ because of who He was and what He had done, or were they turning to a false christ because of the "miracles" that the magic potions did? Were they worshipping the Lord or the cure? Were we leading them to believe that this sorcery is who Jesus is? Were we believing it ourselves?

Stupid question, Kiz. Of course we believed it. Why else would we be swallowing it down by the spoonful and handful and hypodermic full? In the process, we had fully integrated ourselves into the worship of healthcare, not God.

Jesus did leave us instructions for healing. Prayer, fasting, elders anointing with oil and laying on of hands. It was all her search produced. Was anyone else searching? Are you searching the Bible?

We are to partake in the suffering of our Lord. Godly suffering purifies and refines our souls, the most important part of us. The only part that doesn't return to dust. That's the part we are neglecting.

But we refuse to suffer. We fight it every step of the way. We are so addicted to the things of the world that we have no intention of suffering anything. Therefore, we cannot fully know our Lord and Savior.

"...for ye compass sea and land to make one proselyte,
and when he is made, ye make him twofold more the child
of hell than yourselves."
In Matthew 23:15

Kiz went into the corner sorcery store to pick up a tablet. She stood mesmerized, looking at all of the bottles and boxes on the shelves. Cures for everything
it seemed. For some strange reason a deep, suffering, lonely, very sad, fearful
agony slowly crept over her. It dawned on her what was causing this intense
gathering of feelings and emotions. It was what was behind all of this packag-
ing, all of these products.

Genetic engineering on live subjects, chemical testing on thousands upon
thousands of helpless, innocent animals. Forcefully performing abortions on
countless pigs, cows and monkeys. Certain parts being used for medical science
while the rest was ground up and added to our food.

The souls of aborted human fetuses that were being probed as cures for diseases
we "Christians" demanded we be cured of. How many of those aborted fetuses
had been "accidentally" tossed into the food bin to be fed to us? The list of suffering and agony was endless in the name of medicine. Our biggest idol.

While we so-called Christians were screaming for our benefits and cures for
all of our ills, we were desperately scraping at the bottom of the barrel full of
inhumane humanity.

Was this kind of garbage from God? Kiz couldn't believe it was. It had to have
another source. She walked away with a heavy heart, tears in her eyes and a load
on her shoulders. She was fully ashamed that she was part of the human race.

Chapter 33

*"I also will choose their delusions, and will bring their
fears upon them; because when I called, none did answer,
when I spake, they did not hear; but they did evil before Mine
eyes, and chose that in which I delighted not."*
Isaiah 66:4

How many times Kiz had a "feeling" she shouldn't do something, but did it anyway; she couldn't count. It was embarrassing, shameful and humbling to realize it had been the Spirit trying to guide her. God spoke, but she wouldn't listen. She heard, but refused to hear. Some of the things she disobeyed about had no real earthly consequences that she knew of. Many did. Now her ears and mind were, she hoped and prayed, wide open for even the tiniest nudge from the Lord.

This resulted in many puzzle pieces that she couldn't figure out where to put yet. She already knew that evil forces had long tentacles like spider webs that reached into every area and level of our lives, drawing everyone ever tighter and more strangling into it's grasp. She could no longer conceive of the notion that God would have us kept alive with machines, tubes, batteries, drugs, etc. We counted on evil, wicked, pagan rituals to keep us alive.

Kiz knew it was against the law for lawyers to chase ambulances and she strongly believed it should be against the law for ambulances to chase cop cars.

The corner she lived on was where a busy through street intersected a busy four lane main road. There was a lot of traffic and given the lifestyles of a great many in that part of town, there were a lot of impaired drivers. This resulted in many accidents.

Most were fender-benders with no injuries, but at least two ambulances would come screaming in making traffic conditions worse and more congested. Most of the time the ambulances would show up before the police did. She always wondered about that, too. Then she was told that life was precious and should be preserved at all cost. Every minute counts. She thought this was bogus on a great many levels. Tell that to babies that were being aborted.

She soon found out why the ambulances came when not needed. A friend told her that her husband had fallen. She panicked and called 911. It turned out her husband was fine, but they made him go to the hospital anyway. Why? It was now the law. If there was any blood whatsoever, you HAD to be taken to the hospital. The man had scratched his finger and there was one tiny bead of blood.

His insurance had to pay for the ambulance, personnel, emergency room and whatever else they wanted to charge for. Astronomical bills for a nurse or doctor to put a bandaid on your finger and tell you you were going to be alright when you knew all along you would be.

She had also heard a few horror stories about the "authorities" stealing children from parents who didn't make the "proper" medical decisions for them. You WOULD conform or you would be hunted down and prosecuted. A temporary guardian would be assigned who disregarded the wishes of those directly involved.

They would force treatments on the children. Yes, force. People who didn't want to worship that particular beast were being forced to worship it. With new healthcare laws in effect, you would soon have no right to make your own decisions about your own body. Insurance companies and so-called professionals, those with the authority, would be making those decisions for you.

It was already in progress. The medical field seemed to be gathering as much power as law enforcement. Was there really a need for it? It was downright scary. And the world was preparing itself. Healthcare facilities, satellite emergency rooms, urgent care clinics and doctor's offices were springing up on every corner like gas stations.

Kiz found herself wondering at one point if surgical scars would be the mark of the beast, but no, that couldn't be. She found the verse in Revelation. The mark of the beast would be IN the forehead or IN the right hand. That would probably count out a tattoo. Although they were all the rage, too many people were much too vain for that. It had to be something discreet. Hmm…Kiz let it go. She would just refuse anything in those two areas…even if it cost her life.

> *"Lo, children are an heritage of the Lord: and the*
> *fruit of the womb is His reward."*
> Psalm 127:3

> *"And God blessed them, and said unto them, Be fruitful,*
> *and multiply…"*
> In Genesis 1:28

Was that why so many people were influenced not to have children? Because God said to do it? This was Satan's domain anyway. God wanted children, so Satan didn't? And healthcare was helping with this one, too. We were willingly choosing to mutilate the perfect bodies the Lord had created in the pursuit of "no children." Vasectomies, tubal ligation, abortions.

We were even forcing the practices on God's animals. They really weren't ours to tamper with, but we were doing it anyway. Is this what God meant when He gave us dominion over them? Even the law required animal mutilation. City owned pounds wouldn't adopt out an animal unless it was pumped full of chemicals and spayed or neutered.

It's basic right to multiply and it's God-given mandate to reproduce has been stripped from it. Gee…who's idea was that?

Besides being iniquity, all of this healthcare was bankrupting us. Not only on a personal level, but on a national and global level as well.

Kiz knew for a fact that she would never be faced with the decision between drugs and food. There would be no drugs. If she died, she died. It wasn't any big deal to her. Wasn't that our ultimate end on this earth? Why fight it?

The insanity of the world with all of its nonsensical wisdom and know-it-all-ness was weighing heavily on her heart. She was just plain, downright sad. She couldn't see very many Christians turning away from their tests and procedures and life sustaining magic potions to go home to their Lord and Savior. We were too attached to the things and happenings and people of the world. She wasn't finding any faith or trust in the Lord anywhere she looked.

> *"And we know that all things work together for good to them*
> *that love God, to them who are called according*
> *to His purpose."*
> Romans 8:28

This gave Kizzy a light at the end of the tunnel, a glimmer of hope amidst all of the disobedience. Did evil count in that message? It said ALL things. So it must mean evil, too. Yes, now she was sure of it.

All of the sin, evil and iniquity she had committed in her life could have brought her to this yearning to know the Holy Trinity better, to live her life as a pleasing aroma to the Lord. He definitely could and would use evil to further His Kingdom.

It was only by His Grace that she had been plucked out of the devastation that had been her life.

S.S. Riley

Chapter 34

Kiz lay on her bed with her arm over her eyes. She was getting a good chewing out, but didn't know for sure if it was all coming from herself or the Spirit of God. What she did know was that she best take it to heart.

We had all become hypocrites. We kept the outside clean and polished, yet the inside was filty and polluted. Anyone who said they trusted God then turned to sorcery was a liar. Including her. All fifty-seven years of her life.

We worshipped our idols for whatever reasons we chose and allowed pagan rituals and practices to be performed on us in the name of health and comfort, calling on our gods in the Name of Jesus.

Satan was attacking everything and we best be aware of that fact. EVERY-THING. From our soil, air and water to our food supply. Unspeakable things were happening to all creatures, great and small. Everything that affected our well-being. Even we humans. From hours-old infants to the elderly. Our minds and bodies were being played with. There was nothing that wasn't being mutilated and corrupted. No one that wasn't being affected.

Satan wasn't able to do it alone. We were unwittingly, yet willingly, aiding and abetting; destroying ourselves and our enviornment; disrespecting our Creator. All He made, all that He Is and all that He stands for.

If you claimed to be a lawyer or a doctor or a football player or any other professional, there were rules you had to follow. Years of intensive training was involved. Vast amounts of time was spent studying, learning, investing, honing skills, practicing, preparing to be successful, getting in shape, acquiring the proper knowledge and equipment. There was commitment to the way things had to be.

So we claimed to be Christians, followers of our Lord and Savior. Why then was there so little of ANYTHING spent on that endeavor? It was more like Jesus was supposed to be a follower of us. It didn't work like that. Could a surgeon just tack a little note on his door proclaiming he was a surgeon without first knowing what he was supposed to do? When we accepted Jesus as our Lord and Savior, that was the time to crack that Bible open and begin studying, not set it up on a shelf to collect dust.

Had we been tacking little Christian notes on ourselves and then slipping out the back door? Were the lights on, but no one was home? Was the place empty spiritually?

God is ALL IMPORTANT!

When were we going to get that through our thick skulls and hard hearts? There is NOTHING and NO ONE above the Holy Trinity. Not even us. Nothing and no one even came close. Not even us. But we were trying, weren't we?

Why did God really hold such little importance in our lives? People tried to be loving, patient, kind, tolerant and accepting about everything except someone telling them the truth. For some reason we believed we were exempt from it all. Open your eyes, we aren't.

"For whosoever hath, to him shall be given, and he shall
have more abundance: but whosoever hath not, from him
shall be taken away even that he hath."
Matthew 13:12

Kiz kept hearing that it didn't matter what you did or how much time you spent reading the Bible, salvation was salvation. You were saved. She couldn't agree with that on any level whatsoever.

"...to work out your own salvation with
fear and trembling."
In Philippians 2:12

The enormity of what God had done through His Holy, Perfect, Precious, Innocent Son could not be fathomed. What was being done for us on a daily basis couldn't be fathomed either. Invisible spiritual warfare that went on around us constantly. Delights for every sense. The workings of our body that we took for granted. Constant renewal in the world around us. The wonder of life in a tiny seed. The variety of foods we were given. Every single thing we could ever possibly need or desire. The list was virtually endless. All from the Hand, Word and Power of God.

Yet we weren't truly thankful for anything. None of us. We were greedy for more, frittering our lives away on trash. We were taking everything entirely too lightly.

"...to make the Gentiles obedient, by word and deed."
In Romans 15:18

"By Whom we have received grace and apostleship, for
obedience to the faith among all nations,
for His Name."
Romans 1:5

"But be ye doers of the Word, and not hearers only,
deceiving your own selves."
James 1:22

We are the Gentiles! Our spiritual growth, the most important part of us, depended on obedience and trust. Obedience and trust depended on love and familiarity. Love and familiarity depended on reading the Word on a regular basis. It was a lifelong growing process. If we claimed Jesus, but didn't obey, that made us liars. He said so in His Word.

So where was the obedience and trust?

Kiz had prayed for understanding and now wasn't at all sure she was ready for it.

It was clear to her that it was all a matter of the heart. A measure of love you had for your Savior. If she had been reading the Bible all these years for the wrong reasons, what would happen? Did she read it for wisdom, truth and knowledge? Did she read it because she thought she was supposed to? Curiosity? Did she even have a choice as to whether she read it or not? Did she read it because she loved the Lord, wanted to know Him better and know how He expected her to live?

It was time for her to seriously examine her motives. The odd part was, when she did, she couldn't answer any of the questions. Why had she been reading it so much and paying so little attention to what it was really saying? Somehow though, it was finally beginning to sink in.

> *"But I keep under my body, and bring it into subjection:*
> *lest that by any means, when I have preached to others,*
> *I myself should be a castaway."*
> *1 Corinthians 9:27*

She didn't want to be a castaway. She didn't want to be an empty, useless vessel. If she didn't examine her motives very carefully, God would. What was He going to find?

> *"...and the Lord hath chosen thee to be a*
> *peculiar people unto Himself..."*
> *In Deuteronomy 14:2*

It was like looking through a magnifying glass. Yes, we were talking about the Hebrews here, but didn't God's Laws and Commandments apply to ALL of his followers? We were chosen, weren't we?

It was peculiar alright. Look as she might, she could see absolutely no difference between Christians and the secular world. In any area.

We all partook of exactly the same stuff. Were Christians just behaving badly? It needed to be evidenced in our daily lives, but it wasn't. Why would a non-believer even consider becoming a Christian? There were no obvious differences. We were all miserable, we were all caught up in the evil of the world.

The only religious groups that stood out that she could think of were Muslim women, nuns, Amish and Mennonite. They were making a visual statement of their faith. There needed to be something about Christians that the secular world could see and feel. Something out of the ordinary that would make the world take a second look and wonder. Why hadn't we tried to make it believable?

It was true that only God could make the seeds grow, but from what Kiz had seen so far, Christians were sowing the same seeds as everyone else. Whining, complaining, discontent, worry, doubt, contempt, lust, impatience, greed, selfishness, anger, envy, fear, hardheartedness.

> *"But the fruit of the Spirit is love, joy, peace,*
> *long-suffering, gentleness, goodness, faith,*
> *meekness, temperance: against such there is no law."*
> *Galations 5:22,23*

> *"(For the fruit of the Spirit is in all goodness*
> *and righteousness and truth;)"*
> *Ephesians 5:9*

> *"...that we should bring forth fruit unto God,"*
> *In Romans 7:4*

We were so busy "proving" ourselves, chasing after our own interests, that we were unhappy and frustrated. Maybe we needed to spend some of that time ripening those fruits so that the world could actually see them. Then maybe they would want what we were supposed to have. What we said we had, but didn't.

> *"And that which fell among thorns are they, which,*
> *when they have heard, go forth, and are choked*
> *with cares and riches and pleasures of this life,*
> *and bring no fruit to perfection."*
> Luke 8:14

That's what we were. Choked. We were letting the world choke us and for our own good we needed to make it stop. If we spent as much time working on perfecting those fruits as we did on every worthless pursuit we were chasing down, we really might find the joy God wants us to have.

But we weren't about to, were we?

Did that mean we didn't have the Spirit? Is that why no fruit was ripening? A shudder ran through her and a tear slid down her temple into her hairline. She didn't think the shudder was the Spirit moving in her this time.

It felt much more like the stark reality that we weren't even aiming for the mark.

Chapter 35

*"I hate, I despise your feast days, and I will not
smell in your solemn assemblies."*
Amos 5:21

Kiz was trying her best, but as the hardest summer of her life progressed into fall, her angst, depression and craziness burst into full bloom. She decided she did not like the holidays. Not one little bit. None of them. She did everything she could to separate herself from them without being downright rude. If she had her way, she would crawl under a rock and not come out until they were over. It wasn't the spending time with loved ones that bothered her. It was everything the world expected the holidays to be.

First the approach to Thanksgiving. An extremely sad ending to what started as a joyous time. The Indians had helped us survive; they shared their knowledge, seeds, harvest and life skills to keep us alive. Instead of being grateful and respecting their lives and property, we rounded them up, stole all that they had and massacred most of them. We herded survivors into small, usually useless plots of land.

We took their lifestyle, their pride, their country. We killed off their food supply because of greed. Most of the Indians alive today were forced to live in squalor on barren land, their proud, strong heritage stripped from them.

From what she had heard, most were violent, abusive alcoholics and drug addicts. Their suicide rate was extremely high. It was a shame what we had done to them and their once beautiful land…being the Christians that we are.

Kiz didn't need or want the calendar telling her it was time to give thanks. She didn't want to follow the traditions of men. She gave thanks every day of her life. For everything the Good Lord had provided. From the air she breathed to the sleep that took her away and let her mind rest. But most importantly, she was thankful for what Jesus had done on the Cross.

Then there was the stress and expense. Where were we going to eat? Who would be coming? Is the place spotless? Get out the good china. Make sure the fall decorations are perfect. Fight the crowds for lots and lots of expensive food. Who's bringing what? Will everything be done at the same time?

For what purpose? Because the world was telling us to do it? How did any of this bring glory to God? He knew our hearts. We did it because the world expected it from us, not because we were thankful. And always, always, behind the scenes the government was keeping track of every penny we spent. The more money spent, the more successful and prosperous we were. They had no idea what real success was. To them it was all about money.

Christmas was the worst. Christ was being X'd out. Even in Christian homes she saw decoration boxes with Xmas written on them. After all He had done for us, was it too much trouble to write out His Holy Name?

Nowhere could Kiz recall reading in the Bible that we were to buy lots and lots of stuff we didn't need, shower presents on people, spend tons of money we couldn't afford and gorge ourselves with dainties fit for a king. In fact, the whole ritual was contrary to everything the Bible taught.

The WORLD was telling us this is how we must honor the Birth of Christ. The WORD told us something completely different. But we fell right into the world's trap. All Kiz could see was dishonor in the whole process. She wanted no part in any of it.

If we truly wanted to honor the Birth of our Lord Christ Jesus we would do it every day of our miserable lives. Shopping for more stuff, bringing ourselves ever nearer to bankruptcy wasn't showing Godly worship; it was continuance of idol worship on a much grander scale than we did it daily.

Her deprssion worsened. Spending a lot of time on her knees asking for relief from this mental torture brought about some self, soul-searching revelations. There was something within her that was gradually being worked out.

> *"...but he that putteth his trust in Me..."*
> *In Isaiah 57:13*

As the deep freeze and darkness of late January set in, Kiz struggled even more in her afflictions. What was the cause of this and when had it begun? Kiz's friend suggested she was in a dark place and needed help to get out. It was Kiz's firm belief that this was all for a reason and that the Potter's Hand was at work in this darkness.

There would be no turning to pill bottles to pull her out, the cost was too steep. Too many things that were too risky. She had given herself to the Lord, body, mind and soul. There was something to be learned and she would see it through to the end. She smiled and shook her head as she realized she had no choice.

~II~

As temperatures hovered near zero and no end seemed to be in sight, she mourned. Not for herself, but for the homeless. The ones who didn't go to shelters because of addictions and stiff restrictions; for dogs tied to freezing dog houses; for birds that sat in trees; for aborted babies that were being used as cures and food; for rapes, for murders, for addicts, for abuse. For pollution, for unbelievers. Everything weighed heavily on her shoulders.

Kiz was truly miserable because of the burdens of all creation. The suffering and hardship of every living thing made her not want to be alive, to not see anymore of it, to make it all go away.

She knew God was in complete control of it all and had to fight the urge to ask why so much horror was allowed to happen. Deep down she knew the answer - sin and disobedience. Satan's domain.

There didn't seem to be any bright side. Kiz could feel the noose tightening around our free little necks.

We perpetuated lies and twisted the truth. There is no Santa Claus or Easter Bunny or Tooth Fairy. What is wrong with us? Why would we want to break our children's little hearts by telling them the truth? It's as if no one had a brain anymore. We were being led around by a ring in our noses, slaves to the pied piper called the world. We were being driven by dark, unseen forces. Yes, they do exist and we are being deceived by them.

"Finally, my brethren, be strong in the Lord, and in the
Power of His Might."
Ephesians 6:10

She thought she trusted God, she hoped she did, but sometimes she wondered. So she must not fully trust. Satan's powers were stronger than she had ever dreamed they could be. Part of his game was playing on our sympathies and he knew what touched our hearts the most. As each new truth was revealed, her heart broke even further at the condition of the world.

She felt herself becoming weaker and weaker; sadder and sadder, feeling more lost in the world than she ever had before.

Kiz wondered forlornly what joy would feel like. She felt helpless, kept turning to God more often for comfort and guidance. She didn't read the papers or watch the news, but there was always something else to steal what should have been her joy.

One day, on her knees, it was given to her that this was all part of the journey, the ups and downs. There was spiritual growth in progress.

"In your patience possess ye your souls."
Luke 21:19

"and not only so, but we glory in tribulations also: knowing
that tribulation worketh patience; and patience,
experience, and experience, hope: And hope
maketh not ashamed; because the Love of God is shed
abroad by the Holy Ghost which is given unto us."
Romans 5:3-5

Kiz decided to pare back her life even more. With more friends deciding they didn't need her any longer, she had less income to work with. She didn't care about the money part, the Lord would provide. It was the ways in which the friends got rid of her that hurt.

"This book of the Law shall not depart out of thy mouth,
but thou shalt meditate therein day and night, that thou
mayest observe to do according to all that is written
in it: for then thou shalt make thy way prosperous, and then
thou shalt have good success."
Joshua 1:8

Kiz knew that doing nothing wasn't good, so she adopted a slow and steady approach. She kept going, doing what needed to be done. She kept the Lord in the front of her mind. But she couldn't stop thinking and thinking and thinking.

As she worked her way through the days she started to feel solidity when she got on her knees. A sort of physical heaviness like something in her was finally grounded. The sustaining force had to be coming from God. She knew absolutely, for a fact, it wasn't coming from her. She was exhausted again. Plain tired. Mentally, physically, emotionally drained.

She thought that by now, after so long, she would have begun to show some signs of healing, but there didn't seem to be any. Maybe the truth was taking a greater toll on her than she thought. Maybe Satan's attacks were just relentless. Was there something he didn't want her to know? Didn't want her to share with the world? Still, she had no regrets. The connection she had while in prayer was a greater reward than she could have asked for.

*"One thing thou lackest: go thy way. Sell whatsoever
thou hast, and give to the poor, and thou shalt have
Treasure in Heaven…"*
In Mark 10:21

Becoming impoverished by worldy standards had its advantages. We were accustomed to having so much stuff in every area of our lives, we had become ungrateful. We couldn't even tolerate the THOUGHT of poverty. In this life, stuff equaled quality of life. Good quality or bad quality.

Kiz was finding out this was absolutely not the case. Many with much, much more than she had were miserable. She was finding out that poverty pretty much demanded a deeper relationship with God. Building deepest trust, deepest reliance, deepest dependance.

Having a lot required us to go in another direction. Outward rather than inward. This diminished the trust, reliance and dependance to the point that it faded away. They didn't exist in a meaningful way anymore.

The feeling of being truly thankful for something as simple as a hot meal on a cold day while in need was erased by money. Then it was taken for granted, expected.

"…but few are chosen."
In Matthew 22:14

It occurred to Kiz, because of the deep, dark chasm that had been her sinful past, if we had been chosen, God would work in us, grow that seed without us even knowing it. He would bring us to where He wanted us to be according to His Plan for His chosen ones.

It all appeared to be out of control because we had human minds and eyes. But, God was at work everywhere. It wasn't out of control at all. Satan was on a leash.

These reminders cheered her immensely, but for some reason it wouldn't rest.

S.S. Riley

What about all those non-believers? She knew plenty herself and she cared deeply about them. Her mood started downward again. Would this roller-coaster never end? Probably not until she was dead to the world. She moved the unsaved to the top of her prayer list. God would have mercy on who He would have mercy on. Please let it be them.

Kiz's preoccupation with the suffering of the entire world made her question whether or not she could ever experience love. The love we were commanded to have. She doubted it. It seemed like a happy thing. Happy she wasn't.

On her knees during a quiet time it was pointed out to her that she did possess a great deal of love. For God and all His Creation. The suffering she was going through was because of her compassion for the suffering that was going on all around her. If there was no love, there was no compassion. Her love was so great that her own health was in jeopardy because of decreased appetite brought on by the stress of love.

But she didn't worship her health anymore. She smiled. It was all okay.

Satan's well thought out (and so far successful) plan of attack was about to blow up in his ugly face.

In an instant, as if being struck by lightening, it became clear to her. NOTH-ING she was concerned about was in any way under her control. In fact, it wasn't even her business. Yes, indeed, she cared, but, was making herself ill over any of it going to solve one single problem? No. Compassion was a good thing, but not at all helpful under every circumstance.

With the Lord's help, she stripped off the dead, dry, brown cocoonish shell that had restricted her. As she figuratively looked down at it lying useless on the floor, her heart began to soar. Satan had, for awhile, crippled almost her entire being with commisseration. Sadly for him his efforts created something he hadn't intended.

As was supposed to be the case with suffering, it brought growth. She hadn't tried to stifle it. It would do the same for God's other chosen ones. She had to relax and let God do His Work in His Way.

Relax and thank God she did. Maybe extreme distress and discomfort was the ONLY way to get others to a place where they could be redeemed.

"for with Authority commandeth He even the unclean
spirits, and they do obey Him."
In Mark 1:27

With sincere prayer for guidance and an honest desire to understand, Kiz pondered what she had been through and why. It gradually became clear.

She had, in some dark place, felt sorry for herself even though she claimed she didn't. We start setting standards in our life that we refuse to budge from. The way things are going to be. What is acceptable, what isn't acceptable. What we want, what we don't want. How we will feel, how we will not feel.

We expected these standards to be met or else. We expected them from everyone around us or we weren't happy. And we weren't going to let anyone else be happy either. We demanded they comply with what we expected. Even from God. We were hateful control freaks. The key word here is "we." I. Me. I expect and this is the standard you will live up to. Or else.

Christians put themselves in complete control of their lives just like the rest of the world. We are in control and that is that. Sadly though, we are not in control. We are out of control.

When we made the decision to accept Christ as our Lord and Savior, we put ourselves under HIS Authority whether WE liked it or not. Is that why we continued to assume that authority? Because we didn't like His? Why was it called conversion? We hadn't converted from anything. We were overriding the control that was supposed to be His.

Do we really understand what Lord and Master mean? We, because of our own self worship, have put ourselves in the lord position. This brings about all of the lesser idols we worship. Many. It has turned out that we worship everything that conforms to the standards we ourselves have put into place.

It is quite the comfortable little rut we have gotten ourselves into. Whenever God takes us out of our comfort zone, we fight tooth and nail to get back into it. Except that we aren't comfortable and we aren't happy. There is always something else we decide we need to worship. There is always something else we THINK we need eating away at our contentment.

By setting our own standards we are refusing the Lord's Authority over us. It is our way or the highway. We refuse any hardship or lack that doesn't fit into the lifestyle we have created. Are we refusing to let God grow us spiritually?

Kiz realized it really was okay to be helpless and sad.

> *"let the weak say I am strong."*
> *In Joel 3:10*

> *"and God hath chosen the weak things of the world to*
> *confound the things which are mighty."*
> *In 1 Corinthians 1:27*

> *"Therefore I take pleasure in infirmities, in reproaches, in*
> *necessities, in persecutions, in distresses for*
> *Christ's sake: for when I am weak, then am I strong."*
> *2 Corinthians 12:10*

> *"For we also are weak in Him, but we shall live*
> *with Him by the Power of God..."*
> *In 2 Corinthians 13:14*

Our egos demand that we never be weak or give the appearance that we are. We have to be strong, we thrive on power and control. Even when the world we made for ourselves is falling apart, we lie. It isn't okay, but we're going to make it okay. Okay to whom? Our idol selves? Do we ever consider the fact that we are living a big fat lie? Of course not. Then we would be weak. Kiz had learned a great lesson.

~II~

Kiz had a new lightness of being. Winter continued to be extremely cold and miserable, but she no longer was. When she went out into the weather it didn't feel as harsh as it did before. Her spare time was mostly spent doing her jigsaw puzzles, making hats and scarves for the homeless and reading and studying Scripture. Plans were beginning to form for her gardens when spring came.

She still felt in her heart that anyone who took on the responsibility of a dog, then left it tied out in extended subzero temperatures, should be tied out with it. But that was God's call, not hers. They were His dogs.

Satan continued to try to shame and depress her with her past, but she was having no part of it. Many weird and obscure memories would pop up out of the blue. She prayed for all involved, confessed, asked forgiveness, forgave and went on her way. There was nothing she could do about any of it.

None of those things would ever happen again in her life as long as her mind was sound. If it was true, and she believed it was, that nothing could happen to you unless God allowed it, then all of those things happened for specific reasons. She would not be who she was or where she was without them.

"Wherefore I say unto thee, Her sins, which are many, are forgiven; for she loved much: but to whom little is forgiven, the same loveth little."
Luke 7:47

It had been shown to her that she did love much, even when she was sure she didn't. Her search and love of the Word brought forth many things that made her believe she was not crazy after all.

~II~

"They drank wine, and praised the gods of gold, and of silver, of brass, of iron, of wood, and of stone. In the same hour came forth fingers of a man's hand, and wrote over against the candlestick upon the plaister of the

wall of the king's palace: and the king saw the part of
the hand that wrote."
Daniel 5:4,5

What the words written on the wall meant, as awful as they were, didn't much matter; it was the reason they were written that was important.

"And thou his son, O Belshazzar, hast not humbled thine heart,
though thou knewest all this; But hast lifted up thyself
against the Lord of Heaven…"
In Daniel 5:22,23

It was Belshazzar's downfall; his end. Kiz started to lament the fact that we weren't reading the writing on the wall, or our Bibles either. We weren't discerning the signs of the times; we weren't paying any attention to much of anything outside our own little sphere of choice. We weren't looking at the big picture. Things were not boding well for mankind and no one was looking. We were quietly being blindsided.

She let that one go, too. Only God could open our eyes and that would probably only happen if we really wanted it. THAT was nothing she could control.

Chapter 36

"Or if he touch the uncleaness of man, what so ever
uncleanness it be that a man shall be defiled
withal, and it be hid from him; when he knoweth of it,
then he shall be guilty."
Leviticus 5:3

Hey, man, what's going on?

Hello, Paul. Thanks for meeting me here.

Is the bag for me?

Oh yeah, here, if you still want it when we're through.

Thanks, you know I will. Why here? Why not just come to my office like you usually do?

The lake is the most refreshing place I could think of. I just feel so filthy. How can we be so dirty and not realize it? Maybe the breeze will blow some of it off, but I doubt it.

Not feeling so good?

No. That's why I'm so thankful for my faith. At least there's SOMETHING good in this rotten world.

What's in the bag?

Chocolate, walnut, zucchini muffins.

Laney still baking. Yes! Tell her thanks.

My pleasure.

How's the no electronics thing holding up?

Believe it or not, we haven't died because of it.

I see.

Great really. We're all more active and have more energy. A lot of playing catch-up to do. Things are neglected when your nose is glued to a screen all day.

I know.

Things are better, simpler and saner.

So what's eating at you?

I stopped out at Jack's place.

Already? A bit soon for that isn't it?

You know how he claims his produce is organic, just not certified?

Of course. He's been feeding us for years.

It's a lie. A big fat lie.

Jack lies?

Yeah, but I'm not sure he knows he's doing it.

Good muffins.

My seed order came. You know the ones from the heirloom seed company?

Yeah, mine should be coming any day.

Well, I went out to talk to Jack about paying him to get some started for me.

Nice greenhouse he has.

Bought with dirty money in my opinion. Quite a bit of it mine, too.

And mine. Why would you say that? It sounds a little harsh there, pal.

Probably. Sorry. It was just so disgusting.

The greenhouse?

No, the greenhouse was beautiful.

Then?

He was going to mix some soil. We went out back to get bags of vermiculite, top soil and peat moss. That's when I saw it.

Saw what?

What do you know about municipal waste?

That there's way too much of it. As consumers we...

No, Paul, I'm not talking trash pick-up here.

Deprogrammed

Sewage?

Yes. We were talking and I walked to the edge of one of his fields. I couldn't believe what I was seeing.

Should've stuck with carrying bags, huh?

You know?

I'm guessing.

Scattered all over were used condoms, condom wrappers, cotton swabs, blister packs from pills, used tampons, tampon applicators, kotex, diapers, turds, wads of toilet paper. There wasn't just a little bit of it, there was a lot. As far as I could see. A bird picked something up and flew away with it. My stomach turned right there.

You threw up?

I couldn't help it.

At Jack's place?

Yes. Stop rubbing it in.

What you saw isn't the worst of it.

How can you say that? It looked like the worst to me. He said it was all professionally composted and was perfectly safe.

You didn't believe him?

Of course not. Who in their right mind would spread that on their property? Who in their right mind would crawl around in that filth harvesting vegetables? Who would think it was okay to eat that stuff? It was all over all of his fields.

It gets worse.

Couldn't say it got much worse.

It does. Chemicals. They don't compost. What else goes down the drain?

Oh, no.

Prescription drugs being eliminated from our bodies, diseases, bleach, shampoo, cream rinse, toilet cleaner, people rinsing paint brushes…

Manufacturing waste, drain cleaner, vomit, spit, toothpaste, mouthwash, shaving cream. Oh Lord. All in clean, drinking quality water.

It's not the Lord's fault.

He knows it was an expression of "please help us."

Every singlle thing we put down the drain goes into that soup.

It is worse than it looked. And we're eating it.

And it's concentrated. Time released. Every time it rains more gets absorbed into the soil.

Who in the world would even come up with such a stupid idea?

Do you need more than one guess? It's just another solution from the world for a worldly problem. It has to go somewhere.

Every single good thing that God made gets stomped on and turned around.

So we know who's responsible.

We are. Jack said the practice is widespread, practical and completely acceptable.

Deprogrammed

Not to me.

Or me. I s'pose I've duped myself in a way. There won't be any more family outings to Jack's place to stock up on produce. We loved to ooh and ahh at the beauty and variety of the Lord's provision for us.

It's not the bounty's fault. It doesn't know what is going on.

Are you sure about that?

No, now that you mention it, I'm not.

We think we're doing the right thing. We go out of our way and spend extra money to ensure that what we're feeding our family is really good for them, then find out it isn't. Looks can surely be deceiving.

And words, too. We are filthy. All of mankind is a mess.

What are we supposed to do? Is it really as widespread as Jack insinuated it is?

Yep. That's why I made the guess I did. Honestly, it's everywhere. Probably very little we buy from the store wasn't grown in it. On top of that, a lot of our livestock feed is grown in it. The first time I saw it was on a field where feed corn was being planted.

Did you throw up?

No. That was probably twenty years ago. I was shocked though. It gave me food for thought and prayer for a long time.

That many years? We've been dumping that toxic concoction on the earth for that long? Imagine how concentrated it must be by now.

Truthfully, between runoff and a lot of it being sucked up by plants, there probably isn't a big concentration.

S.S. Riley

Except in the water. Vicious, evil circle.

That reminds me of two other things.

Such as…?

First, all of this stuff we put into water. I heard someone say scientists can't figure out how to get prescription drugs out of the water.

But can the water get out of the drugs?

What?

Maybe the water will evaporate and leave the residue behind. You think that could happen?

I don't know. I never thought about that. I suppose it's possible. Unless somehow it has become molecularly bonded to the water itself.

Then it ceases to be water anymore. It has become something else.

But we still call that something else water.

Of course. What else would we call it?

Dunno. Depends on what is bonded to it.

You think there could be thousands of new elements?

It's very probable. But I'm not a scientist and don't plan to ever become one. Only they could say for sure. And I don't think I want to know the answer.

Me either. Just something else that nothing can or will be done about.

You said two things.

Yeah. The drought in California.

Pretty bad, isn't it?

Makes me wonder. Other places are getting pounded with rain. Epic flooding.

So what about it?

They've put a lot of restrictions in place, but I don't understand why people continue to go to the bathroom in water that we could be drinking. It makes no sense to me.

Now that you brought it up, it isn't very smart is it? But what's the alternative? A porta-john on every corner? Nobody's going to go for that.

I know. Then we have even more polluted solid waste to dump on the ground. I wonder if Abraham thought it was a good thing when God told him his descendants would be as the sand on the shore if it could be counted.

We do have a lot of serious problems, don't we?

There's always the toilet-to-tap program.

Don't even get me started on that one. Irradiate it to kill whatever's left in the water. Just what I want to drink, a bunch of dead disease germs and spores. Yuck. Maybe they just get mutilated and aren't really dead.

Oh, Lord.

So…is Jack going to start your seeds for you?

Just like that you get all nonchalant? No. He isn't. I didn't get to that point. I didn't ask. I was too ill. I'll start them myself somehow. What do you know about building a greenhouse?

Really good muffins.

Chapter 37

*"For I am not ashamed of the Gospel of Christ: for it is the
Power of God unto salvation to everyone that believeth;
to the Jew first and also to the Greek.*

*"For therein is the righteousness of God revealed from faith to
faith: as it is written, The just shall live by faith.*

*"For the wrath of God is revealed from Heaven against all
ungodliness and unrighteousness of men, who hold the
truth in unrighteousness:*

*"Because that which may be known of God is manifest
in them; for God hath shewed it unto them.*

*"For the invisible things of Him from the creation of the world
are clearly seen, being understood by the things that
are made, even His Eternal Power and Godhead; so that they
are without excuse:*

*"Because that, when they knew God, they glorified
Him not as God, neither were thankful; but became
vain in their imaginations, and their foolish
heart was darkened.*

"Professing themselves to be wise, they became fools.

*"And changed the glory of the Uncorruptible God into an
image made like to corruptible man, and to birds,
and four footed beasts, and creeping things.*

*"Wherefore God also gave them up to uncleanness
through the lusts of their own hearts, to dishonour their
own bodies between themselves:*

*"Who changed the truth of God into a lie, and worshipped
and served the creature more than the Creator, Who
is blessed for ever. Amen.*

*"For this cause God gave them up unto vile
affections; for even their women did change
the natural use into that which is against nature:*

*"And likewise also men, leaving the natural use of
the woman, burned in their lust one toward
another; men with men working that which is
unseemly, and receiving in themselves that
recompense of their error which was meet.*

*"And even as they did not like to retain God in their
knowledge, God gave them over to a reprobate mind,
to do those things which are not convenient;*

*"Being filled with all unrighteousness, fornication, wickedness,
covetousness, maliciousness, Full of envy, murder,
debate, deceit, malignity, whisperers,*

*"Backbiters, haters of God, despiteful, proud,
boasters, inventors of evil things, disobedient to parents,*

*"Without understanding, covenent breakers, without
natural affection, implacable, unmerciful:*

S.S. Riley

*"Who knowing the judgment of God, that they which
commit such things are worthy of death, not only
do the same, but have pleasure in them
that do them."*
Romans 1:16-32

It sounded a lot like what Kiz had been seeing in the Churches she had attended. An extension of the rest of the world. History repeats itself. Or maybe we just never tried to quit sinning. She took it upon herself to know exactly what every one of those sinful words meant. She looked each up in her dictionary and meditated on their meanings.

In prayer, she asked God to show her the faults that needed to be corrected to please Him. She knew she wouldn't or couldn't ever be perfect in her human form, but she loved God and didn't want to purposely hurt Him. She made sincere efforts to curb the things that were shown to her.

When she walked, she took slow deliberate steps. Thought before she spoke. Swallowed anything that could be considered as gossip or meanness, criticism or judgment. Unless it was called for. We are to rebuke our brethren.

She did speak of some things when sharing a burden. We are allowed to share our burdens. When that happened she kept her words to a minimum, watched her tone of voice, refrained from whining, didn't complain and didn't elaborate into gossipy mode.

Information and insight still kept coming to her, seemingly to assure her that she wasn't crazy and the things that had been given to her were correct. Like believing that higher education was evil.

The debt for college education had exceeded all other debt combined. Homes, cars, boats, business, credit cards, everything. Didn't the Bible tell us we were to owe no man?

Most of that money was loaned by the government. Borrowed from China? What was going to happen when the money was due and no one could pay because jobs were few and far between?

Maybe the same thing that was going to happen when foreign countries wanted their money back. It was a trap. Satan liked to set traps we had to sell ourselves to get out of. When our kids, or us for that matter, couldn't pay, the government would pretty much own the debtor. What were we going to have to do to pay back all that money we owed? The outlook wasn't good. The kind of education we were going to get wasn't good. Worldly wisdom wasn't good.

Kiz oftentimes wished that time could reverse itself. She honestly wished she could go back to the good-old-days. She missed them. People talked instead of staring at their phones all day. They made do with what they had. They used their brains instead of their credit cards. TV was an hour or two of family time instead of a lifestyle or babysitter.

People actually did things instead of sitting around all day. God designed our bodies for movement. Satan wanted us immobile, sedentary.

But our idols wouldn't allow us to live quiet, simple lives. We were stuck serving them, acquiring more and more stuff to look at. Did we understand what lust of the eyes meant? What would the good-old-days mean to these younger generations? Kiz shuddered.

Getting off those lines of thought, she drifted back to the Word. She loved the Bible. It felt more like the real world to her than the real world did. After extended periods of reading and study, it was difficult to come back to her worldly responsibilities. But they were hers, they had to be dealt with. The Lord had put certain things in her life and she respected that.

Kiz knew she was ready to go home. Where ever that might be. If Jesus cast her to His Left, it would be the greatest moment of her being to have met Him. Whatever His decision was, there was only one place she deserved to be. She was sure of that.

> *"…and there is no new thing under the sun."*
> *Ecclesiastes 1:9*

It was a complete mystery to her how what had been shown to her counted as anything. All of what she perceived to be the truth gained from the Spirit of

God was available to anyone who wanted access. It was all given to her through the media, print, over airwaves and through cables. The information must be widely known to be making the circuits as it was. What made all of that so special? And why had it affected her so deeply?

Kiz felt that it had all afflicted her in a very negative way over a long period of time. She had known she was in trouble when she told her daughter all she wanted was a shotgun blast to the head. Kizzy smiled as she thought about how far she had come since that day.

What was the catalyst that had done all of this? No one seemed to be as upset about any of it as she.

Then she was gently reminded that she had prayed for her faculties to be opened to understand the truth. And apparently they had been. It gave her the ability to put it all together and see the direction the world was taking us.

She wasn't completely, 100% sure yet, but the conclusions she was starting to draw were downright scary. Waiting was her only option.

Once more she was being drawn back to the friends, the faces, the fellowship she had enjoyed with the people around the impoverished lake area. She was beginning to miss them desperately.

Going back to the idol worshipping Church was out of the question. Her time there was finished and she knew it. The way she felt about the Church establishment now pretty much counted them all out. As much as she yearned to be part of the Christian family, she didn't want to go back to a Church.

There were a few other places in the area where she might volunteer. In her heart it was where she wanted to be. She would start asking around. Wherever she ended up, the Lord's Hand would be in it.

Gradually, under continued trust in God, she felt the eerie feeling that something was terribly wrong was coming to a head. Scripture was the key to understanding.

"And they rejected His Statutes, and His Covenant
that He made with their fathers, and His Testimonies which
He testified against them; and they followed vanity, and became
vain, and went after the heathen that were round
about them, concerning whom the Lord had charged
them, that they should not do like them."
2 Kings 17:15

Guilty as charged.

"For the wrath of God is revealed from Heaven against all
ungodliness and unrighteousness of men, who hold
the truth in unrighteousness;"
In Romans 1:18

Guilty of that one, too. We have no idea what God's Righteousness is.

"Because that when they knew God, they glorified Him not as
God, neither were thankful; but became vain in their
imaginations, and their foolish heart was darkened.
Professing themselves to be wise, they became fools."
Romans 1:21,22

Who? Me? Never! Yeah, right, Ditto. Guilty. All of us.

She knew what Christians were doing.

When the Ten Commandments were ignored and broken on a daily basis, what importance could the rest of the Bible have? Not much, she concluded.

Kiz realized from her studies that there were many strings attached to being a follower of Christ. We had either broken those strings or never grabbed on to them in the first place. Had we been deceived to believe that, oh well, our sins are washed clean so what does it matter? It did matter. A lot. We are to repent.

Two verses where Jesus spoke stuck out clearly in her mind.

> *"Not every one that saith unto Me, Lord, Lord, shall
> enter into the Kingdom of Heaven; but he that doeth the
> Will of My Father which is in Heaven."*
> Matthew 7:21

> *"But why call ye Me, Lord, Lord, and do not the
> things which I say?"*
> Luke 6:46

Scary stuff. It deserved to be taken to heart. What had happened to the souls of the believers Ananias, Sapphira and Judas? Kiz shuddered.

And as she pondered these things and wondered what she was going to do with all of this "bad news" that had been delivered to her, the Voice spoke.

Write your story.

What? Lord, if that's even You, I am not wise in any way. I am a nobody. I didn't even finish high school. I am a quitter, not a writer. No one listens to me. I am a joke. I am an outcast.

You are in good company.

What will I do with it if I ever get it finished?

The name. It will be given to you later. When the time is right.

Why me? Why is it always me?

> *"This I say therefore, and testify in the Lord, that ye
> henceforth walk not as other Gentiles walk, in the
> vanity of their mind."*
> Ephesians 4:17

> *"...And might perfect that which is lacking in your faith."*
> In 1 Thessalonians 3:10

It suddenly became clear to her that the "last days" were from the time of Jesus' birth on. We were in the last days. The events as recorded in the Book of Revelation were playing out. They were happening. The signs of the times were glaringly well under way. But who cared? Who was watching? Who was putting two and two together? A few maybe, but not many.

How far we had progressed into the Book was unclear. Only God knew. But we had progressed over two thousand years into it. The New Babylon was being rebuilt. She saw it in one of those documentaries her son was so fond of.

What upset Kiz the most was that we were already conditioned for the trap. We were so accepting and tolerant of everything, especially technology and healthcare, that we were eagerly embracing each step forward.

Satan was tricky. His mark was going to appear to be a godsend, making our harried lives safer, more convenient, more secure, easier. Because we never gave a thought of any real value to anything we did, we were going to be swarming to get his mark. Bragging that we got the ultimate in technology, we were free now, we were safe. And we didn't even know what we were doing. It was the latest fad.

The "something terrible was happening" head finally burst. Every bit of the truth that was in it, along with all of the disgusting pus and blood and guts, blew up right into her face. Kiz's knees weakened and she dropped.

We, as Christians, are as guilty in this onward march toward total destruction as the evil secular world is. We are up to our necks in it. And we are going to suffer for it along with the unsaved. It is as much our fault as it is theirs.

Why?

Because we ignored the Words we were to live by.

Because we are EVERYTHING Jesus Commanded us not to be.

Because we ARE the world He warned us to stay out of.

But we just wouldn't listen, would we?

We did, what we thought, was right in our own eyes.

So, now what?

Are you absolutely certain you are ready for…

THE END

?